SILVER CHIEF'S REVENGE

SILVER CHIEF'S

Revenge

BY JACK O'BRIEN

Illustrated by Kurt Wiese

HOLT, RINEHART AND WINSTON
New York / Chicago / San Francisco

PUBLISHED SEPTEMBER, 1954
SECOND PRINTING, NOVEMBER, 1954
THIRD PRINTING, MAY, 1956
FOURTH PRINTING, JANUARY, 1962
FIFTH PRINTING, JANUARY, 1964

Library of Congress Card Number: 54-5071

96239-1012

Printed in the United States of America

This book is dedicated to my pal
JOHN FAIRFAX CUTRER

Grateful acknowledgment is made to the following agencies for their friendly co-operation and technical information:

THE ROYAL CANADIAN MOUNTED POLICE
Ottawa, Canada

THE CANADIAN CONSULATE
of New York City

THE FEDERAL BUREAU OF INVESTIGATION
Washington, D. C.

THE UNITED STATES AIR FORCE
Pentagon, Washington, D. C.

Contents

Chapter 1

MURDER

SILVER CHIEF's tail thumped a lazy good morning to his master, Sergeant Peter Thorne of the Royal Canadian Mounted Police. The big dog's greeting was acknowledged when Thorne dumped a cascade of freshly chopped wood beside the cheerful potbellied stove which stood in the center of their rustic cabin. This cabin was a combined office and home; it stood in a clearing in the Canadian woods across the Great Bear River from Fort Norman, in the Mackenzie District of the Northwest territory.

The blond, blue-eyed sergeant rubbed his wet boot good-naturedly along Silver Chief's spine as he wiped the melting snowflakes from his own eyebrows and hair.

"Up and at 'em, Chief. Out of my way so I can rustle some breakfast for us."

Silver Chief merely rolled his eyes up toward Thorne and cocked one ear as if to say he understood the nature of the joking between them.

Thorne filled his tea billy with water and set it to singing on the stove. As he commenced to mix the batter for wheat cakes he switched on the powerful, yet compact, all-wave radio set that stood on a rough pine desk near his bunk. Next he opened two cans of dog food, dumped it into a pan, and set it on the stove. Silver Chief raised his head a fraction of an inch to observe with critical eye whether his breakfast was being prepared. Within minutes the snug little cabin was filled with the aroma of a simple yet well-cooked meal. Bacon sputtering, flapjacks rising, tea water boiling, a succulent aroma coming up from Silver Chief's dish, and the radio sputtered and clacked as Thorne switched from one station to another. First the world-wide news, then back to the routine police calls, then away again all over the vast frozen North Country of upper western Canada, picking up the various weather fronts and newsworthy items to be recorded in his logbook. Thorne ate his breakfast and tried to do several things simultaneously.

Silver Chief stood near the fire, methodically gobbling his breakfast in as little time as possible.

The weather broadcast from the huge U.S. Air Base at Fairbanks, Alaska, was coming through with monotonous, rhythmic clarity . . . "Temperature minus three degrees Fahrenheit; wind fourteen miles per hour east to west . . . Ceiling seven hundred . . . Visibility three hundred and poor . . . Forecast is snow and warmer."

Suddenly Sergeant Thorne stiffened in his chair, tense with concentration. Even Silver Chief stopped gulping and poised his head, attentive and alert. A voice, low and urgently pitched, broke into the broadcast.

"Mayday! . . . Mayday! . . . CQ. . . . CQ. . . . Mayday! . . . Being forced down at gun point . . .

Being forced to crash-land. . . . CQ. CQ. My position approximately 64° 58′ North by 125° 53′ West. Landry calling . . ." This was hastily repeated, and then silence—deep, hard, dramatic silence. The voice of the weather broadcaster came on, a trifle shrill from excitement. "Did you get that? . . . All stations, that was a CQ—and a Mayday. To anyone listening, 'Mayday' is the International Distress Signal . . . We are plotting the location. Will broadcast within a few minutes . . . Stand by . . ."

Without waiting for further word, Thorne crossed the room in a bound and turned a switch that flooded light upon the wall map thumbtacked along the entire side of the cabin. Glancing briefly at his notes, he brought his pencil to a point on the map and held it without movement for a full half-minute as he studied the map closely. Suddenly he snapped his fingers at Silver Chief.

"That's us, boy. About six miles from here. C'mon, we've got work to do."

Silver Chief pricked his ears forward and barked a short, joyous answer. Thorne switched on his two-way radio and called the Royal Canadian Mounted Police Headquarters. As soon as his signal was acknowledged, he spoke into the microphone:

"Sergeant Peter Thorne, Fort Norman District, reporting."

A distant voice crackled back in answer, "Go ahead, Sergeant Thorne, we read you loud and clear."

Thorne continued. "The Mayday emergency I just picked up is about six miles from here. I am leaving on a search patrol in fifteen minutes with my dog, Silver Chief. Am on snowshoes. Over."

From a peaceful, relaxed man, enjoying his break-
fast and the joy of welcoming a new day, Sergeant
Thorne instantly became the trained guardian of the
Canadian territory to which he had been assigned.

Outside, minutes later, Thorne scanned the sky. It
was an early cold January morning. A piercing dry
snow drove into his upturned face. He gauged the
visibility and unfavorable weather conditions as
closely as a merchant scanning diamonds; for with
each man it could be a matter of life and death to use
his judgment correctly—one false movement meant
disaster.

Silver Chief, alert and sniffing the wind and snow
himself for his own telltale signs, realized his master
was off on no trivial, routine inspection trip. He
watched intently as Thorne tightened the web belt
around his waist from which hung a thoroughly oiled
revolver in its polished holster. Silver Chief could see
that his master wore an old and trusted rawhide sling
over one shoulder, rather than the usual dress-white
cord line that kept a Mountie from ever dropping
his revolver, be it in the snow, mud, or even accidentally on parade.

As Silver Chief edged up to his master, the wind
ruffled his gray-white coat, showing the pure white
fur underneath. He came to his master's side as they
stood ready to go.

Peter Thorne sloshed through the snow to the lee
side of the cabin where the cut and stacked wood,
the tools, the ten gallons of kerosene and the snowshoes were all stacked under a crudely built lean-to
adjoining the cabin.

He slipped his waterproof field boots into the

snowshoe thongs and tied the rawhide bindings that secured the shoe at each heel. While still shrugging on his pack, containing a first-aid kit, two blankets, sufficient field rations for three days and extra ammunition, Thorne took a quick bearing and was off with long, measured strides, his head bent against the icy, stinging snow.

Silver Chief ranged first ahead, then behind the silent, purposeful man who never deviated from his course, across slash timber, silent, grim, rock outcroppings, through quiet woods where the snow fell softer and served to intensify the hush of the deep North Country, which is known as "hump-land." The whoosh-whoosh of Thorne's snowshoes was the only sound in that vast, eerie world. One word of command, "heel," brought Silver Chief into the track behind Sergeant Thorne as they commenced a gradual, yet steady ascent through the broken and scarred timber.

Thorne made frequent pauses to check by compass and to glance at a small grid map carried in a leather pouch. Now he was nearing the bearing flashed on the radio. A final three hundred yards of ascending brought the two to the top of a hill overlooking a wide area of the countryside.

The panorama spreading before them was a desolate waste of bog and lake, swamp blending into water hummocks of forsaken land, runted and bent trees, with occasionally a break as though a meadow or a clearing might exist under the white blanket of snow.

Thorne drew out his binoculars and, shielding them as best he could from the falling snow, carefully scanned the surrounding country. Silver Chief stood erect and still as a marble statue, his keen nose quartering the wind for any scent that might reveal unseen danger.

Thorne muttered a sharp word of surprise and glued his glasses on a spot to his left and far down the forward slope, perhaps half a mile away.

"There it is, Chief, it's a plane's tail sticking up all right. H'mmm . . . No fire . . . Looks like it belly-flopped into some sort of clearing. C'mon, let's go. . . . Easy now."

Thorne and Silver Chief silently drifted downhill, melting into the trees and brush like ghosts.

A few minutes later they had arrived at the scene of the crash. Thorne did not immediately approach the wreckage, but stooped behind a dead, blackened tree stump and peered cautiously around it. Silver Chief crouched alert at his side, as his master carefully parted a clump of brittle twigs.

From what he could see, Thorne guessed that the pilot had spotted an opening in the forests and tried to land without skis, on what must have appeared to be a fairly smooth patch of ground. However, it was obvious that he had not been able to see the hidden hummocks and snow-covered snaggled stumps that lay beneath. The plane had not been demolished, and appeared to have almost made the landing safely, but then nosed over. Ripping out the wheel assembly, smashing the propeller, and half tearing off a wing, it had remained, tail up in the air like a burrowing hedgehog. There was very little snow piled up on the wings and fuselage; this convinced Thorne that here was the plane he had been seeking.

After a few more minutes of close study, he and

Silver Chief cautiously emerged into the clearing and circled the Royal Canadian Air Force plane. The door to the cabin swung desolately to and fro in the wind. Thorne bent down and untied the bindings on his snowshoes, bidding Silver Chief to stand. He tested the canted fuselage to see if it would pull down level. When it did not budge, he lifted himself with an easy motion into the cabin of the plane. Silver Chief stood below, glancing around uneasily, the hackles lifting along his scruff, a low, deeply imbedded growl coming from his throat. As Thorne stuck his head out of the cabin door, a feeling of uneasiness communicated itself to him because of Silver Chief's actions.

"What is it, boy? What've you got? Something wrong?"

Silver Chief looked up once, as if trying to answer, not moving, yet visibly impatient to be released from his command to stand.

Understanding his dog so well and having had a hand in his training, Thorne knew that Silver Chief was trying to convey an important message, and yet, gazing down at his loyal assistant, the sergeant could not quite read the exact meaning behind Chief's tense, alert attitude. He jumped down to examine the tracks around the damaged plane, but they belonged only to himself and Silver Chief. Whatever was disturbing his dog must lie beneath the layer of snow—perhaps some action which had taken place when the plane cracked up. Now Silver Chief was looking up, and quivering with a desire to wander off. Thorne released him with the one word, "Go!"

Like a flash the dog bounded away, his nose alternately skimming the snow, rising to test the wind. With swift, sure instinct he started to circle the plane, his course ever widening, sniffing at every rock and tree trunk, fallen branches, bent-over saw grass and other places exposed by the drifting snow.

An experienced tracking dog, Silver Chief knew that rain and snow wipe away the scent. He must therefore seek the spoor, the telltale clue left behind by every living thing. Often those spoors clung in the air or around brushed-against trees for days at a time —both human and animal spoors. Furiously testing the wind, Silver Chief realized that the quarry he sought was human!

For a few moments the sergeant watched the alert animal industriously pursue his chore, then the sergeant bucked into the cabin of the plane and slithered forward toward the badly damaged cockpit.

Though larger than the average bush plane of the Canadian and Alaskan Far North, this was obviously a type belonging to the Royal Canadian Air Force. Inside the cabin, at the base of the connecting fire wall, all was a mass of twisted, piled-up wreckage. Fire extinguishers, tools and all the paraphernalia of flying were thrown into a scrambled heap.

He was surprised to find the door open and capable of being swung almost into the cockpit. After pushing through the doorframe, he stopped short, heart pounding against his chest. Though he had had much experience with human tragedy, Peter Thorne had never become hard. He was especially touched by deeds of valor. Thus the sight before him made him catch his breath. There was Pilot Landry, strapped to the seat, hands still on the controls of his ship, but slumped over in the unmistakable attitude of death!

Both pity and admiration welled up for the brave man who, loyal to his training and ideals, had held fast to responsibility to the end. Squirming past the wreckage, Thorne carefully examined the controls. He then turned to Pilot Landry, appraising the exact position of the dead man's body. A keen eye and techniques used to solve past problems made the sergeant alert to every detail. Intuition also served to sweep away matters unrelated to the situation. An idea came to him, dimly at first, but then with a shock for its apparent possibility . . . The pilot's face and head were unmarked. Furthermore, his head was at least two and a half feet from the shattered windshield. Yet, over Landry's drooping shoulders, his arms and body, over the seat and floor, lay dark, hard-caked blood. Perhaps . . .

Half kneeling, Thorne examined the body at close range. Deep in concentration, he did not stop upon hearing a short, triumphant bark from Silver Chief. His dog was signaling, and by the tone, it seemed likely that Chief had come upon a warm, live scent. Carefully, methodically, Thorne continued his examination, but paused once more, distracted by another sound. From far off came a dull throbbing that increased in volume to the clearly recognizable roar of an airplane engine.

Curious, the sergeant tried to peer through the cracked, frosted windshield, but it was impossible to see out. Besides, he decided that most likely the oncoming plane contained another searching party of those who had also heard the pilot's frantic plea for help. There in the Far North, the code of bush pilots demanded that help be given, no matter how hazardous or far away. In those treacherous, far-reaching distances, there was the ever-present possibility that each might need to call for friendly assistance.

The engine's drone now hovering above confirmed Thorne's idea that the immediate terrain was being studied before an attempted landing. But before he investigated, there was a more pressing problem. What had caused Pilot Landry's death?

Finally he traced the direction of dried blood to a spot between Landry's helmet and the fur collar on his leather jacket. Had something struck from above? Glancing up, Thorne discovered that the radio and generator box had been torn loose from their moorings. The weight of these fallen objects could have been the cause of death. It would have been simple to accept this evidence. Because Thorne had been trained to take nothing for granted, he never assumed a fact without definite proof.

To eliminate all doubt, he pried loose the pilot's blood-caked collar, unstrapped his helmet and pulled it slowly from Landry's head. Gazing down at the wide, exposed area of flesh, Thorne's eyes narrowed and the muscles of his cheeks stood out solid and rigid. The time consumed for the careful examination had been completely justified.

He had discovered the unexpected!

Just below the line where head and shoulders joined was a small blackened hole, no bigger than a pencil point. All too clearly the tragic story was now revealed. Pilot Landry had been shot in the back by a coward's hand, who clearly had no provocation for the attack! As a subject of the Queen and an officer of the Royal Canadian Air Force, this murderer would be hunted down by every available law-enforcing group. But to Thorne, who had found the helpless victim strapped to his seat and struck unaware from behind, the case was not merely one in the line of duty, but a deeply felt personal matter.

He scrambled up the sloping plane to the door and, without pausing, flung himself through the opening to drop ten feet into the snow. Thorne ignored his snowshoes, which lay faintly snow-powdered beside the plane and floundered wildly through the drifts, out onto the clearing. There he saw the small bush plane bearing down in a final approach before landing.

Since he was better able to visualize the terrain than the approaching pilot, he signaled for a landing to the left, thus avoiding a mass of uneven hummocks. The pilot responded at once, veering to the proper position. Through light-falling snow, Thorne saw the little plane—with its distinctive green markings—hang poised for a moment before settling on its stork-like skis, to send up a cloud of snow spume when they touched the ground.

Dimly, through the roar of the engine, the sergeant again heard the barking of Silver Chief. This time, though faint and far away, Thorne detected a new note in the message from the dog. The barks were prolonged, yet sharply marked and urgent. Intent now to reach the radio in the plane to report Pilot Landry's death, Thorne let Chief's signaled warning go unheeded.

Even after the plane had come to a complete stop,

its propeller ticking over in slow, lazy revolutions, the sergeant could see heavily bundled figures moving aft to unlatch the door. He waded through the snow, flailing his arms and shouting hoarsely. Just as he came up around the wing the door opened.

A huge man struck his head out and shouted in deep guttural tones:

"Vaslovich! Is that you?"

Chapter 2

SURPRISE ATTACK

THORNE stopped dead in his tracks. Instead of some messenger of mercy, he was confronted by a vicious-looking stranger, who stood there in utter disbelief, because in place of Vaslovich he was facing Sergeant Thorne.

In that moment of mute surprise, the sergeant rapped out sharply:

"Who are you? What are you doing here?"

As an answer the man whirled back into the plane, shouting orders with great authority. "Stelka, alert, an enemy!" Then after a muffled reply sounded from within, he spoke again. "Chelkar! At him, Chelkar!"

Fully alert to danger, Thorne reached for his holster to draw, but he was a split second too late. A great, ugly brute of an animal leaped from the plane and launched itself at the sergeant. In one bound, the dog, Chelkar, clamped fanglike teeth into Thorne's heavy field-coat sleeve. Though Thorne wrenched with all his strength, Chelkar bit deeper and deeper, trying to tear through bone and flesh.

Turning this way and that to be rid of his tormentor, Thorne saw, out of the corner of his eye, the man called Stelka join his unsavory companion. They both scrambled down from the fuselage to take positions on opposite sides of the struggling Mountie. Their silent watching infuriated Thorne, sending him into feverish action. He worked the glove of his left hand free and grasped the animal's throat with his bare hand. His fingers then sought the iron-studded collar, which he grasped firmly; then, with a tremendous wrench, Thorne loosed the brute's grip and sent it sprawling aside into the snow.

His brief advantage acted as a signal for both men to leap toward him. Again having no time to draw, Thorne drove his fist straight into the face of his nearest opponent. There was grim satisfaction in feeling his knuckles grind against the man who had given orders for Chelkar's attack. From the way the man flung orders around, Thorne supposed that he must be the boss. But boss or no, the space between his heavy fur collar and blue-knit stocking cap had made a perfect target for the sergeant's punch. At the sound of the smashing impact Stelka cried out:

"I'm coming, Illych. I will help you."

Thorne noted this name; he also observed that the bewhiskered face of the leader seemed vaguely out of balance. One of his eyes was crossed, giving a slightly comic look to the stranger's anger. There was no more time to notice, for the fury of fight descended on Peter Thorne as he was taken by a low, hard tackle from the rear. Knowing that no rules of decency would be observed by such ruffians, Thorne did not hesitate to kick back with his free leg. There followed a hoarse cry of pain and wail of protest from the sniveling Stelka:

"Oh, Illych! He has broken my face!"

The grunt that his leader gave was accompanied by a sudden sound of gunshot from nearby. When this sharp report did not halt Stelka's whining, his unfeeling friend spoke with contempt.

"Silence, Stelka. Perhaps that shot came from Vaslovich. He may be in trouble."

Then Thorne remembered his dog's previous barking. Could Chief's quarry have been the one with whom these strangers had their rendezvous? He had no more time then for questions or speculation. A sudden, searing pain shot through him.

Chelkar, his ears laid back, his body slinking close to the ground, had cunningly attacked from the rear to gnash at Thorne's thrashing leg, which he now held in a steady, viselike grip. Whipcord breeches were like tissue paper between teeth that ever increased their pressure.

Waves of nausea almost overpowering him, Thorne struck out wildly, at the same time trying to maneuver his leg to be rid of the beast. With Thorne's attention turned briefly to the dog, Illych reached into a pocket, withdrew a leather buckshot-filled blackjack and brought it crashing down on the sergeant's head.

Thorne felt himself being clutched by waving arms, felt a brief contact with dank, smelly bodies; he reeled and tilted, sensing more than actually knowing what was taking place. The blackjack struck again and, with a sickening sense of release, Peter Thorne lost consciousness.

Illych watched as his victim fell forward in the snow, then with a savage kick he sent the huge dog sprawling away from Thorne's torn, bleeding leg.

Stelka had a look of near admiration as he gazed down on the sergeant's inert form. "Some man," he observed, stepping over Thorne to secure Chelkar by his collar.

But Illych seemed in no mood to follow this line of thought. "Never mind that!" he snapped. "You can let go of the dog; we have much to do."

The leader paused then as if in reflection. "There is the wrecked plane," he said, "but where is Igam? That shot—you heard it, Stelka. It may have come from the spot of our actual rendezvous. Perhaps Comrade Vaslovich fired—perhaps an enemy. At any rate, we must be cautious."

"We must be cautious," Stelka echoed, wiping his bloody nose on a thick, dirty mitten. He went on almost pleading, "We had better hurry. I am sure my nose is broken. The blood is freezing. Soon I will not be able to see when it swells up. Then you will have no pilot."

This warning did not penetrate through Illych's self-pity. "You should talk," he growled. "That creature there, who resembles a police officer, has robbed me of two front teeth. Here," he showed his face in a gaping grin, blood oozing from his mouth as he spoke. "You complain, when every breath I take in this freezing air is torture. Be quiet now and do what you are told!"

Through flakes of snow that had become larger and widely spaced, the two men moved over to the wreckage. Their own plane, perched firmly on its skis, still had the propeller idling at almost a stalling speed.

Illych stopped just short of the upended plane fuselage and carefully looked around the ground be-

neath it. Seeing no signs of activity, he peered into the
wrecked cabin. With a curt motion he signaled his
companion to step beneath the cabin door, and to
bend over. Wordlessly Stelka did as he was bidden.
Illych hoisted his bulk up, Indian fashion, so that he
was half in the cabin, standing on Stelka's back. In a
moment he stepped down, apparently satisfied with
his search.

"Gone, everything gone. . . . Now we go to the
rendezvous. Igam Vaslovich has done a good job.
This will be remembered. He will be recommended.
Everything has gone according to schedule. But we
must hurry. We are tardy because that fool blundered
upon our landing. Where is our rendezvous spot?"

"Igam said it would be the lightning-blasted pine,
one kilometer due north of the center of the landing.
It is on a slight rise. We will be able to see the trunk.
Impossible to detect him until we creep through the
underbrush. It was planned so, in the event another
plane flew over the area before we reach our destination." This information was parroted in a manner of
one speaking from memory. "Let us go then," Stelka
added.

Illych's reply was simply a low grunt.

Wordlessly they strode toward the north line of
trees on their right, cutting across the clearing at a
diagonal to reach the center. Presently Illych, who
had been peering constantly to his right, stopped and
grunted again. Stelka, covering his nose against the
cold and snow, also paused. Silently they gazed at
each other before turning into the thick underbrush
along the side of the clearing.

Soon Illych, pushing and brushing his way through

snapping branches and heavy frozen underbrush, stopped short before a blackened, barkless tree stump that shot one lonely stalk into the sky. He glanced around and nudged his companion.

"This seems to be the place," he said. "But where is Igam?"

Not knowing, Stelka shook his head.

The two stood surveying the scene of a fierce and bloody struggle. Though there was no sign of their Comrade, Igam Vaslovich, evidence pointed to the fact that he had been there. Near the stump, bright patches of blood lay bold against the snow. Illych soon discovered that these tracks led in the opposite direction from the plane. He dropped down for a moment to examine the prints better.

"Igam was attacked by some animal," he observed. "Probably a wolf, judging from the size of the tracks."

Meanwhile Stelka was searching in the hollow of the tree stump. His stiff, mittened fingers groped deep beneath a spongy layer of leaves. Suddenly his finger tips struck something hard, something far too smooth and regular to be part of the blackened growth. Almost unbelieving, he traced the contours of a compact, rectangular box. Igam had managed to hide the cache before he had been attacked!

"Here, Illych!" he cried. "Here in this hollow is what we seek!"

Illych joined Stelka, and they both dropped to their knees to peer down on the lucky find. The leader was the first to rise. As he spoke, his tones combined pleasure and craftiness.

"What luck," he said quietly. "Igam has given us perfect means for escape. Surely he cannot survive long in this wilderness. He must die; this will throw the scent from us. This is extremely fortunate for the Cause."

Stelka gazed at the disappearing tracks that told of the dreary flight into the forest. He slowly shook his head in protest before turning to his leader. "But Igam is one of us," he murmured. "We cannot leave him here to perish."

"Be quiet, Stelka. I am in command. First things first. We have found what we were ordered to get and must waste no time in searching for Vaslovich. Help me to the plane now with this box."

Still Stelka argued. "But Igam is my friend. He could not have gone far into the wilderness, especially after so much loss of blood. It would not take much time to search."

With slow deliberation Illych straightened to full height. The tempo of his gestures studiously measured, he felt inside a pocket and withdrew a pair of thick, rimless glasses. When he put them on, his expression became stern, autocratic, as if the lenses not only corrected his crooked eye but also gave him special powers.

"Every man must be prepared to give his life for his country," he said loftily.

"But . . ."

"This is an order. Now, at once, help me!"

Stelka shrugged. "For our country then," he said in tones of irony. He leaned over, assisting his Comrade to dislodge the box which suction held fast against the damp sod below. Struggling and panting, they finally managed to raise the heavy burden from its place.

Slowly they made their way through the woods and across the clearing to their green-trimmed monoplane. Illych ordered the box to be set down directly in front of the hatch. Then he turned and moved to the still-inert form of Peter Thorne, whose face was half buried in the snow. He coolly observed the sergeant's labored breathing before nudging the half-frozen face with the toe of his shoe.

"Look there, Stelka," he said, "and you can see what I mean. There is the product of this stupid system in which we are at present forced to abide. See him lying there like a sack of rags. Chelkar alone could have finished him. . . . And they give themselves airs about the Individual. Huh! When the fine Canadian police get through with their inspection, they will stupidly conclude that Igam killed both the pilot and this intruder. They will deduce that Comrade Vaslovich got away with the box. These Individuals!"

"This man will surely freeze," Stelka replied absently.

"Oh, no! We will not trust to that! Here," Illych glanced at his watch. "We are behind schedule," he continued impatiently. "Grab Chelkar—there under the wing—and throw him into the plane. Then, Comrade Stelka, shoot this man. And aim straight, mind you!"

Chapter 3

SILVER CHIEF IS WOUNDED

MEANWHILE, Silver Chief, released by his master's "Go," had bounded off on his own mission, circling the plane, his nose skimming the snow, his bushy tail waving and erect. Several times he paused to look back to be sure Thorne did not need him.

On his fourth and ever-widening course around the plane, Chief stopped beside a rock outcropping on the edge of the timber line. A scent, faint and yet curiously rancid, still clung to an exposed bit of lichen moss growing on the lee side of the rock, away from the elements.

Chief stood as still as the forest around him, as he sniffed carefully trying to detect more telltale signs to suggest direction. The odor was definitely man-smell. Moving cautiously around the rock, he discovered another rubbed-off place which also carried the scent. Judging this position from the first clue, the direction he must take was into the woods. With redoubled alertness, he moved off toward his goal.

At last Chief came upon the direct scent he'd been tracking. He stopped short, blending with a tangle

of brush in perfect camouflage. The man-made odor
was now dangerously close, but the sound of an
approaching plane briefly diverted the dog's attention. Chief raised his head, as if to decide whether
the machine-bird overhead had discovered his hiding place. When it winged past, he was assured,
and crept toward the now overpowering scent. Using
every bit of cover at his disposal, he circled the focal
point until he stood upwind a little above where he
judged the enemy lay in cover. Now, half crouching,
half slinking, he began to stalk his prey.

A descendant of purebreds, and sired by another
famous Silver Chief, whose deeds of valor were
legend in the North Country, young Chief had traits
permitting him to respond with daring and intelligence to unusual situations. Combined with this fine
heritage, he had been trained in the exacting tradition of the Royal Canadian Mounted Police, and he
knew well that the moment had come to combine
courage and true cunning.

He inched forward, belly almost dragging the
snow, muscles rippling in matchless co-ordinated
strength, his sharp eyes sweeping every inch of
ground. Slowly he crept toward the lightning-blasted
tree, planning to use the shadows at its base for
protection color. Raising his head to peer about,
Silver Chief spied a gray silhouette raising arms from
out of the hollow stump. Then, as if he too had a
sense of danger, the man wheeled suddenly, staring
in startled wonder at his pursuer.

After a brief, silent pause, both moved simultaneously. Chief gathered his legs beneath him and

sprang. At the same moment the stranger reached in his pocket, whisked out a revolver and fired. There was a spurt of smoke and flame searing the dog's fine coat at the shoulder, a sharp report, a stab of pain—then Silver Chief was on the man—eighty pounds of dynamic fury.

The full force of the attack fell upon the upraised hand holding the revolver. The man reeled back, his weapon sliding down upon the trampled snow. With strength born of sheer terror, Igam Vaslovich regained his feet and staggered blindly backward, as he wildly hammered at the animal that was relentlessly crushing his forearm. As his fist came down again and again, Igam noted blood spreading on Silver Chief's coat. His shot had found its mark, and this fact renewed his courage.

Fiercely and with tremendous effort, the two fought their way to the site of a huge hemlock tree. With a desperate motion that lifted Silver Chief from the ground, Vaslovich swung in an arc, sending the dog crashing against the tree with a fearful impact. The force of the blow dazed the animal, driving the breath from him. Fighting for air, Chief's grip on the man relaxed, and with a wrench, Vaslovich was free. He gave a sob of fear and turned to dash deeper and deeper into the forest.

For a few minutes Silver Chief lay stunned, then he slowly struggled to his feet, clearing his head by a vigorous shake. He sniffed. The trail of his enemy was fresh and easy to follow, yet, in some strange way, Chief realized that tracking the brutal stranger could continue later on. An awareness of his master came upon him, and he turned to hurry, as fast as his wounded leg would permit, toward the clearing.

After passing the hollow tree, Chief limped beyond to the timber line and halted to peer out. From a cove of protective shadows, he spied two strangers coming directly toward him. Instinctively the dog summed up a plan of action. Since these unknown persons were facing a glare from sunrays that now were attempting to break through the gray overcast, Chief decided to be bold and direct.

The canny animal flattened himself as close to the

snow as possible, wriggled directly into the clearing,
then headed for the opposite timber line. Not once
did the gait of the strangers waver to suggest that
they had noticed Silver Chief. Having passed their
line of vision, the dog rose from his crawling to take
sanctuary among gnarled rotted trees and frozen
brush. After a brief respite, Silver Chief moved to a
spot where, though still hidden, he could gaze down
at the place from which he had started. Eyes toward
the wrecked plane, his ears pricked forward, his nose
became wet and quivering as he sampled the wind.

From odors wafted his way, Chief could partially sense what had taken place. He caught the familiar scent of his master—there was blood-smell too. Chief's pulse quickened with excitement—dog smell! Also, the strangers who passed awhile before had left telling human spoors on bits of shrubbery. A feeling of unnamed danger all around came over Chief, lifting his upper lip into a snarl.

He made a few hesitant steps into the open. From this vantage point he could see an inert form lying in the snow. Nearby a huge ferocious animal stood guard. Sensing that he might have to do battle with this creature, Silver Chief carefully licked his wounds in prelude to the possible combat.

He was about to continue, but sounds of feet crunching against the snow and the snapping of twigs suggested further caution. Chief backed into the shrubbery and watched the men he had seen before, return. This time they were carrying a heavy object between them. The dog stared as they moved clumsily toward the plane, and bristled at the tremendous size of the dog rising to greet them.

Then suddenly, without specific reason, the soft prompting of duty became an urgent summoning. *At once, now!* And Silver Chief leaped forward! He must attack that creature, whose gaping jaws and ropelike muscles clearly belonged to an enemy! Full awareness came to Chief, even before his widespread legs carried him to his destination. Danger was no longer general, but sinister and directed against his master. It belonged to the man who now disappeared into the plane—to the dog hoisted in after him—

to the shorter man who turned suddenly and pulled a revolver from his pocket, pointing it. Then came a shot, directed at—at—*his master!* The man with the gun would have had time to fire again, but for some reason, he did not.

Because of his wounded leg, even Chief's crazy rage could not drive him swiftly enough to overtake the foe. Bracing himself, he skidded to a stop, just as the plane began taxiing down the hummock field. With a roar and a huge kickback of snow, the plane was airborne.

Panting, Silver Chief moved to the side of his master. He sniffed the cold face and ran his nose exploringly down over the snow-banked body. His master was still breathing. His master was alive! Feverishly the dog went to work, ignoring his own injury. He hastily pawed away the snow around Thorne's face and head. Crouching down, Chief snuggled as close as possible to his master in an effort to communicate his own body heat to the unconscious man. Gently he licked Thorne's face, giving special attention to an exposed ear. Steadily and patiently the dog tried to restore life in the only way he knew.

Gradually Thorne showed signs of returning consciousness. At first the stirrings were so faint as to be scarcely discernible—a fluttering eyelid, his mouth opening to admit more air, a vague motion of the body—and finally Peter Thorne opened his eyes. Moaning, he felt the back of his head, where the twice-descending blackjack had raised two enormous lumps. Soon aware of Silver Chief's warm body against his, the sergeant tried to lean over and pat his loyal friend. A wave of weakness overcame him again, and he lay quiet, attempting to collect his thoughts.

After resting for a while, Thorne forced himself upward from the ground, remaining briefly on hands and knees and shaking his head to try to clear it. Then, by force, he wrenched himself erect, clenching his teeth at the pain searing through his leg. A glance at his shredded trousers—stiff and blood-clotted— brought his memory into full focus. Before making plans or trying to go on, the sergeant unwound his scarf and wrapped it tightly above his wound as a kind of tourniquet. At least now he would not bleed to death! Time for action, he decided as he gazed toward the wrecked RCAF plane.

Before venturing forth, Thorne turned in gratitude toward his faithful companion. "Good work, boy," he murmured. "Thank—" Words were halted by the sight of blood matted on Silver Chief's chest and leg. "They got you, too! Here, Chief!"

Thorne gently washed the wound with snow and applied an antiseptic and a dressing from his first-aid kit. As he worked deftly to make his dog as comfortable as possible, the sergeant mused:

"Hmmm—this is a rough crew we're after. Murder, shootings, assault, everything in the books. Wonder what it's all about. Something big to make them go to such lengths, it seems to me. Whoa, Chief. Stand still. Did you see them, boy? Which way did they go?"

Chief barked a sharp response and started in the direction of the blackened tree stump. "Where do

you think you're going?" Thorne demanded, and
when the dog continued, his master stopped him
with a sharp command to heel.

"It's back to the plane for us," Thorne continued.
"Search parties will surely come and then we can
broadcast the news of Landry's death."

As they approached the plane, Thorne spied his
snowshoes, now almost completely covered under a
layer of white. Pain made him clumsy in his move-
ments, but he managed to kick the snow off and slide
his feet into place. Glancing at his watch, the sergeant
discovered that several hours had passed since the
crash. Landry's call for help should have been heard
before this. Thorne could not just wait around.

Sensing that his master was in conflict, Chief
whined and darted forward, turning his head in
pleading to be followed.

"All right, Chief, we'll try it your way," Thorne
said.

Eager and alert, Chief retraced his course, but
moved with caution as they approached the blackened stump. Satisfied that no danger now lay hidden
at that spot, he approached directly the hollowed-out
remnant of a tree and furiously sniffed at the ground
around it.

Using his flashlight, Thorne leaned over to peer
into the shadows of the stump. Damp leaves had been
pushed aside, and below he could see bold, direct
lines, suggesting that some object had been recently
removed.

While he was studying these marks, Silver Chief
gave a series of excited barks that turned into angry

snarlings. Thorne looked down where Chief was
scratching at a dark object in the snow. The sergeant
leaned over and dislodged a mud-caked automatic
revolver. He looked from the weapon to his dog.

"Is this what got you, boy?" he said. "Well, we've
got *it* now. A good thing too. Maybe this also got
Pilot Landry. At any rate, it's the first bit of Crown
evidence we have to produce. Come on, let's at 'em!"

Chapter 4

MAN HUNT

SILVER CHIEF immediately assumed that he'd been given permission to take over. Holding his head high, he sniffed and quartered the wind from all directions, tail stiff as a ramrod, body tense.

"What are we looking for, Chief?" the sergeant asked. "Let's get busy."

Chief started off in ever-widening circles, his nose to the ground, searching for a clue to get back on the scent. About twenty yards from the blackened tree stump, the dog gave a short, excited bark, stopped and turned, eyes pleading with his master to follow. Nothing more was needed. Thorne knew that the animal had come across a warm, live scent.

With his ability to face grave dangers and arrive at quick decisions, the sergeant followed Silver Chief into the forbidding forest. Thorne felt certain that search parties would soon find the smashed plane, and that if he remained, first aid would be available. But he knew also that time thus gained by the escaping criminal would possibly mean his complete get-away through the trackless, gloomy forest. Then, too, the sergeant's decision not to wait was prompted by the code of the Mounties, contained in the world-famous, oft-repeated slogan, "Get Your Man!" Far better to endure unknown dangers and hardships than betray one's ideals!

They plodded on. Whenever Chief lost the direct scent and started coursing wildly back and forth, Thorne would take time for a compass reading, to approximate the direction in which they were headed. The wrecked plane had been due west from Fort Norman; now they moved roughly at a north-westerly slant, which took them above and away from the garrison. Thorne racked his brains for a likely hiding place in the deserted wilderness. To the best of his knowledge all the country on that side of the great Mackenzie River was studded with virgin timber. He realized, of course, that lonely shacks might be concealed within scooped-out clearings, and that sinister forest shadows could prove a sanctuary for a fleeing fugitive. He would have to place his trust in Silver Chief.

His dog's sense of direction had always been a source of wonder to Peter Thorne; and he marveled at it now. Snow had transformed the land with deceptive skill; hump-land was smoothed out, depressions filled in, and objects which might have been used for identification were now unrecognizable. Even for the most expert woodsman snow became a deadly enemy, in spite of the soft innocence of its mantle. Apparently this phantom did not bother the purposeful animal leading the way through the tractless, gloomy woods.

As Chief moved farther and farther from civilization, Thorne pondered on the meaning of recent events. . . . The death of Pilot Landry. . . . The

savage attack he himself had suffered. Those blows
on the head were meant to kill! And he saw again
the face of a man—bearded and with a slightly
crossed eye. Recalling him, Thorne smiled briefly,
grinding bruised knuckles into the mitt of his other
hand. One thug was going to remember the Royal
Canadian Mounted Police for a while anyway!

A thought that had been running through his
mind now became a piece of the puzzle which was his
to solve. Recalling the bearded man had been a par-
tial answer. But it was Chief who suddenly furnished
further proof.

The dog, who had been ranging steadily ahead,
stopped short near a twisted hemlock trunk, sniffing
furiously until his master caught up with him.
Guided to a portion of the trunk, Thorne found out
what had excited Silver Chief. On the rough bark
about twenty inches from the ground the sergeant
made out a dark-brown blotch. Almost invisible
against the brown of the trunk, it was Chief's sharp
nose that first traced the stain. It was blood, somewhat dried, but unmistakably fresh! Thorne rubbed
Chief's ears in gratitude and patted him fondly for
this first sign that they were closing in on their
quarry.

Thorne spoke then, half to himself, half to his
faithful friend. "That's it, Chief. Blood about a half-
hour old. Whoever left this stain cannot be too far
ahead of us now. It came to me just a few seconds
ago that you barked a warning *before* the green-
trimmed plane landed. Someone was already there,
eh, Chief? You were trying to tell me so. That was
what threw me off, but I understand now. The per-

son we're after might be one of the gang and going
to a prearranged hiding place. No telling at this
point what we are getting into, Chief."

Thorne cast a worried look over his shoulder at
the pale sun, cold and remote in the gray overcast
above. He judged that not much more daylight remained before the dread night of a North Canadian
winter would be upon them, and made a grim, silent
resolution to meet with the escaping fugitive before
nightfall.

Slowly they pushed through the forest, where the
cold, lifeless silence became increasingly more sinister. Added to hardships caused by nature's winter
plan, the pain from their wounds increased, tempting
them to stop and rest awhile. But the waning day,
the fugitive ahead, drove them relentlessly forward.

Presently, against the awesome silence, Thorne
heard a baffling sound. Not that it was unfamiliar,
but there in that bleak and forsaken woods it was
difficult to place. Thorne called softly to his dog,
and as they stood there quietly listening, he realized
what was surprising about the break in silence. Believing that he was not near any settlers, he had not
expected to hear the baying of dogs. Chief became
immediately alert, his ears pointed straight ahead, a
low growl coming from his throat. Cautiously man
and dog moved forward toward the rising din, and
stopped at the edge of a clearing to peer out into the
gathering dusk.

Ahead stood a small cabin, scarcely more than a
shack except that it had a chimney, from which smoke
was rising lazily upward. Obviously the place was
occupied.

Near the back of the shack, tethered in approved North-woods style, were nine great crossbred Malemute dogs. All barked in one hideous cacophony of sound as they bayed for their supper. Thorne also saw the silhouette of a big komatik pack sled stacked against the wall of the cabin. After carefully considering the terrain, the sled and pack before him, Thorne realized that he had come upon one of the shacks owned by No-kaw-i, a famous half-Indian, half-Eskimo fur trapper. The sergeant had seen his pack and sled before, and No-kaw-i's scattered shacks were legend around that part of the country.

Thorne knew that No-kaw-i ranged all over the territory around Fort Norman, disregarding property lines, Crown land, and even the fenced-off uranium claims. Indeed, Thorne had on a few occasions spoken to the half-breed about such freedom of movement, but No-kaw-i stubbornly maintained that he had been trapping in those parts long before anyone but the trappers had set foot near Fort Norman. From his own point of view this was sufficient excuse to continue.

No-kaw-i was a silent man of the woods, visiting Fort Norman only when absolutely necessary. He was known to be a peerless trapper, to have the finest dogs, the best-built sled and the finest pelts in the country. This small shack was one of many which No-kaw-i had constructed along his many trap lines, in the event of a blizzard when he was away from his main camp.

Though the half-breed was sometimes surly and taciturn, Thorne doubted any connection between him and the deadly murder in the clearing. He had, however, seen too much of crime not to admit that anything was possible in the strange frozen land of the Far North. Besides, Silver Chief had come directly to this spot, which could harbor others besides the Indian.

The sergeant knew that it would be foolhardy to try to surprise his quarry when restless dogs were staked so near the cabin. His only chance of achieving the unexpected would be to use the age-old military action—the flanking movement!

Quietly he ordered Silver Chief to remain while he slipped off into the woods, going around and downwind from the sled dogs. After completing a half-circle, the sergeant crouched down on the opposite side of the clearing. He cupped his hands to his mouth and gave forth with the haunting, eerie screech of the great white Arctic horn owl. Immediately Chief broke from cover and trotted close to the tethered dogs. The sight of an intruder sent the entire pack into a wild frenzy of barking and snarling which rent the air in a warning. Chief was content merely to dash along the fringe of the pack, then move off again into the safety of the forest.

Exactly as the sergeant had hoped, the door of the cabin flung open and a figure emerged, rounding to the rear of the shack. Thorne pulled out his revolver, snapping the safety catch to "off," then limped warily to the clearing, while cries came from the dogs as the figure laid about them with a rawhide whip.

The Mountie crept through the half-open cabin door, every sense alert. He heard a grunt of surprise and the motion of a body as he whirled about. On a rough pine bunk built onto the cabin wall lay a

man, one arm wrapped in a thick, clumsy bandage.
Thorne raised his revolver, pointing it squarely between the stranger's eyes. He motioned for silence,
and, for a few moments, the quiet tableau held.

Outside, the dogs settled into a cowed whimper.
A brief pause, and the cabin door swung in. No-kaw-i
stepped into the fire glow. When he saw Thorne deep
within the cabin, his revolver drawn, the trapper's
stern, immobile face went even more blank with
astonishment. Suddenly he burst into a torrent of
pidgin Indian and Eskimo phrases, his voice rising
in excitement, as he repeatedly pointed to the
stranger on the bunk. Even though the Mountie had
some knowledge of the dialects used, it was difficult
to follow the spouting, frantic speech. Before Thorne
had a chance to make much sense of it, the dogs outside again set up a din. Even though he kept his
attention on the prisoners, the sergeant could see out
of the corner of his eye what had caused the new
commotion. Silver Chief, with the calm assurance of
knowing himself wanted, ambled confidently into
the cabin.

Thorne smiled. "Here, Chief," he ordered, not
lowering his head. "Over here."

Unlike his usual obedient self, the dog did not
seem to hear his master. Instead, he became suddenly
taut, sniffed and then whirled about to snarl at the
man on the bunk in deep-throated anger.

Chief seldom took immediate dislikes, but if his
master was surprised by this conduct, the reaction
of the injured man was infinitely more startling. His
terror at being confronted by the angry animal
seemed far greater than having Thorne's revolver

thrust into his face. With a hoarse cry he pulled the blanket over his head, as if trying to rid himself of an awful dream. Obviously this man and Silver Chief had met before. They had; he was Igam Vaslovich!

"How did this man get here?" the sergeant demanded sternly of No-kaw-i.

Again No-kaw-i waved his arms wildly and burst into a torrent of Eskimo phrases.

"Slow down so I can understand," Thorne said more kindly.

After many minutes of brief questions and lengthy answers, the Mountie realized that No-kaw-i had merely been another victim of a fugitive's treachery.

No-kaw-i, it seemed, after having returned from a hunting trip, had been brutally struck on the head upon entering his cabin. After regaining consciousness, the trapper came upon his assailant outside, where he was trying to harness the dogs.

"Dog sled's one way to get off in a hurry with a bum arm," Thorne commented. "What happened then?"

No-kaw-i had armed himself, brought the man indoors and held him prisoner, he said. After this explanation the half-breed became taciturn again, no doubt feeling hostile because of the sergeant's suspicions. After a brief defensive look, he moved to the stove and began to stir the pots of food that were cooking.

Darkness had fallen, and the aroma of supper tempted Thorne to remain awhile and eat and relax. Now that he had the situation under control, a little more time might not matter too much. But he pushed the thought away. The longer they remained, the

more difficult it would be to get their prisoner to
Fort Norman.

"Stow the grub and put out the fire," he ordered
the Indian.

The trapper muttered under his breath, but notic-
ing the look in the Mountie's eyes, decided to obey.
After the flames paled and flickered out, he told
No-kaw-i to go out and harness the dogs.

Again the Indian protested, grumbling about the
perils of a North Canadian winter night. But Thorne
was adamant. Leaving Silver Chief to guard the
wounded man, he escorted the reluctant Indian into
the cold. The snow had stopped; No-kaw-i threw one
beseeching look toward his snug warm cabin, but
Thorne prodded him on. With a shrug, the half-
breed buttoned a beautiful fur parka tight around
his throat as he walked to the rear, shouting to rouse
the bedded-in dogs. About twenty minutes later, after
much barking and yelping and full use of the rawhide whip, the komatik was ready, with dogs in position, lying in the snow waiting for their master to
start them off.

Thorne sent the half-breed inside to make sure
that the prisoner Vaslovich was warmly dressed; he
would be the one riding on the sled. When they came
out, Thorne explained the order of their travel. The
wounded man was to be driven to Fort Norman,
No-kaw-i standing on the runners of the sled, Thorne
behind him on snowshoes and Silver Chief bringing
up the rear.

A crack of the whip, a strange cry, and No-kaw-i
had his team up and straining under the load of their
cargo. Occasionally as they traveled, the sergeant

called for a halt so that he and Silver Chief could
rest. Both the dog and he were limping badly and
suffering great pain and fatigue. It was grueling to
keep up with the pace of the mighty, well-trained
team of dogs. That long stretch through the dark
almost impenetrable forest was achieved by outstanding courage. The sergeant knew that his prisoner,
though heavy-lidded, was fully awake and alert. To
relax vigilance might well prove fatal. They must
keep up with the sled—far better that hardship than
drifting around in the snowy wilderness where many
men had been lost. Lost, yes, and not to be found
until spring—a frozen testament of the power and
cruelty of the country in which they lived!

About midnight the night-duty officer at the Fort
Norman police station was startled to see three men
enter the building, stiff-legged and almost falling
from exhaustion. One of them stood slightly in the
rear of the others, pointing a revolver and directing
the two to move up to the desk. Not until Silver
Chief limped in did the officer recognize Sergeant
Peter Thorne. The man before him, grim, bespat-
tered, his face pale and lined with pain and weariness,
was most unlike the spruce Mountie he had so often
seen in action. This evidently was no brawl between
some of the town's less desirable citizens. This was
a serious matter that confronted him. The sergeant
looked as though he was about to collapse. The
policeman drew his revolver as he sprang from his
chair.

Swaying, his voice rasping with fatigue, Thorne
addressed the police officer.

"Sergeant Thorne, here. Royal Canadian Mounted Police. I'm bringing in this man whose name and address are unknown. . . . Charge is wilful and premeditated murder." He indicated Vaslovich with a wave of the revolver and continued weakly: "Revolver here to be used as Crown evidence. Mark it Exhibit A. Also send out all-point broadcast at once. Two men flying a green-and-white monoplane. Bush type. Occupants on scene of murder. I can identify. Probably accessories."

"Right you are, Sergeant. What about the other man?"

"Keep him here." Thorne seemed almost unable to go on. "But—I—believe he was forced to harbor —this—this—"

"Sergeant, you're hurt!" the officer exclaimed. "Better sit down."

Suddenly the heat of the room and all that Thorne had endured took its toll. Previous events seemed unreal, far away. The only thread of comfort remaining was that he had gotten his man. . . . He began to feel himself falling, pain in every limb. Slumping forward, he was enveloped in a merciful blackness.

Chapter 5

GUILTY

I N THORNE's dream a huge gray-green wave, dark, cresting and threatening, rushed toward the shore, faster, faster and faster than Peter Thorne could swim to safety. He glanced back over his shoulder twice and saw that he would never be able to reach the beach before he was caught. With a convulsive effort he turned his body in the raging sea and faced the towering monster that hovered for a sickening instant before it crashed. Down, down he sank into the sea-green depths, fighting and gasping for breath, trying to free himself from the whirling frenzy of the raging surf. His lungs seemed to be bursting, his arms stilled their furious threshing, and he knew he was drowning without aid, without a chance! The last horrible groan of his life bubbled from his lips.

Slowly, as through a distant haze, his eyes and his senses focused upon reality. Upon the blessed and real sound of a human voice. Thorne struggled to sit erect, but was gently forced back. At last he realized he was alive, as his head sank back to the comfort of an eider-down pillow.

"Here, here now, Sergeant, what's all the shouting

and groaning about? Sounds like you had a bit of the
horrors in your dreams."

Bending over him was a white-jacketed attendant
who peered intently into his face.

Thorne looked around the white room wildly,
then spoke.

"Where am I? What happened?" he asked. "Where
is Silver Chief? What am I doing here? Speak up,
man. What's going on here?"

"Take it easy, Sergeant. You're in an Air Force
Base Hospital. You and your prisoners arrived at
Fort Norman in bad shape about midnight last night.
They flew you and your dog here in a 'copter. It's
now Saturday morning. We're all glad you pulled
out of it at last."

Thorne showed his impatience by speaking
sharply.

"What's this all about? Speak up. Where's Silver
Chief?"

"No need to excite yourself, Sergeant. Your dog is
fine. Other than that, all of us here at the hospital
are under orders not to speak to you, nor allow anyone to speak to you before you see the Inspector.
He asked to see you the minute you came to.

"You must be on to something big, is what I say.
Even that dog of yours rates a private room—and a
guard." The orderly shook his head in bewilderment
at the strange behavior of his fellow man. He walked
toward the door.

"Take it easy now, Sergeant. I'll fetch the Inspector."

Thorne lay back in his hospital bed trying to recall
the events that had put him in a condition where

he did not know what day it was, where he was or
what had happened to cause this state. He was becoming calmer now and felt sorry for speaking sharply to
the orderly. The fellow was only carrying out instructions.

Footsteps sounded in the hall, and the door to
Thorne's room swung open and was held respectfully
by the orderly. The sergeant gasped and automat-
ically tried to stiffen to attention and salute, for in
walked Inspector Corliss, who was not only Thorne's
superior, but the chief officer of the whole Western
Division of the Royal Canadian Mounted Police.

The intrepid Inspector, hawk-faced, trim, erect,
with a fearless look in his eyes, strode briskly into
the room, waving for Thorne to relax. Going directly
to the patient's bed, Corliss shook his hand with a
firm, friendly grip. Though Inspector Corliss moved
with precision and spoke in tones of clipped authority, he still had the look of a man who could listen,
and pass fair judgment as well.

"Glad to see you pulled through, Thorne," he said.
"Pretty filthy business you ran into. We're all proud
that you delivered your man."

These words stirred Thorne's memory with faint
ideas to explain his present plight. He answered
simply, "Thank you, sir."

The Inspector continued, "Haven't seen you since
that situation down in Victoriaville. Had something
to do with your horse, didn't it?"

"Yes—Royal Red."

"And that fine Indian boy. What was his name?"
asked the Inspector.

"Tiwa LaHache, sir."

"Tiwa, that's right. Did us all a great service. I read the testimony of that trial." The Inspector then dropped all pretense of making a social call when he asked, "How are you feeling, Thorne? I mean really —not just to be polite. This is business."

As always, Thorne spoke with direct honesty.

"I'm not quite sure how I do feel, Inspector. My mind is still a little vague. I must have been hurt— there's a bandage on my leg. I feel a little tired and beat up; otherwise, fine."

The Inspector smiled. "A little beat up—huh? I must say that's the understatement of the year, from what I've heard. But to get on . . .

"I'm up here on orders. It's my job to keep an eye on you, secure information from you and direct your action as soon as your health permits."

"I'll co-operate in every way I can," Thorne promised.

"I'm sure you will." Here the Inspector sighed. "But I have a feeling that many important facts will remain obscure. You see, Thorne, the situation in which you have become involved goes far beyond the murder of Pilot Landry. It is the motive for the murder we are after. To find out the motive is the reason another branch of the Government wants you."

Thorne's memory had now fully returned, and yet he could not quite understand why the events in which he had become entangled should warrant so much investigation. "But why?" he asked.

"Even *I* don't know," the Inspector told him. "So don't ask questions I can't answer."

"Sorry, sir."

After Thorne reported all that had happened the

day before, the Inspector turned and bellowed
through the hall, "Orderly . . . I say, Orderly. Get
the doctor here and the chief surgeon. On the double,
lad. Hear me?"

"Yes, sir," came a startled voice.

While they waited, Thorne could not help asking,
"Who was the prisoner I brought in?"

"Even that I can't say positively, Thorne. He
claims to be a Canadian citizen, though obviously
he's not. He has papers avowing citizenship, and will
be temporarily accepted as such and tried for murder
under the name he has palmed off. But there is more
to this situation than meets the eye. As soon as you're
strong enough to dictate, we want your deposition
so we can get the trial going with little or no delay.
Again, these are orders.

"Furthermore, my instructions are that you will
put into your deposition only those facts dealing directly with the prisoner. Everything else will be made
on a separate report. Evidently they don't want other
testimony made public information at this man's
trial.

"Shocking business, the wrecked plane and Pilot
Landry. Again I commend you for bringing in the
murderer."

"Are you sure this *is* the murderer?"

"Without question. His fingerprints were all over
the inside of the fuselage as well as the pilot's compartment. They were also on the mike that the prisoner evidently ripped off when Pilot Landry called
for help. The bullet that killed Landry matches the
ones in the prisoner's revolver. This was determined

in the post-mortem examination. An open-and-shut case."

"Looks that way, sir. But what puzzles me is, why? What grudge prompted him to go to such lengths. What does the prisoner say?"

"Not much," the Inspector replied. "He calls himself Fred Daroff and he is curiously stoical and silent about himself. He seems resigned to the worst. Repeats his name over and over, his former address in East Canada, and nothing else. His behavior is much like that of a prisoner of war."

"H'mmm." Thorne was thinking of the definite instructions issued to Canadian troops if captured during the war . . .

Corliss interrupted Thorne's thoughts. "Yes," he said. "The man acts as if his silence is ordered. Nothing will trick him into talking. Incidentally, we almost got the two men in the green-and-white monoplane."

The sergeant looked up with interest. "So? What happened, Inspector?"

"An Air Force search plane that flew over the scene of the murder picked up the monoplane on its radar, followed it for fifty miles due south and notified the Base here. Unfortunately, our plane was following a search pattern and had to do a ninety-degree turn north and so lost track of the monoplane. However, three hours later, when we began a routine check of all planes aloft and on the ground, we found that the green-and-white monoplane had landed in Dawson City, near the Alaskan border, had refueled and taken off again.

"The constable in Dawson City talked with the airport manager, who remembers there were two men and a dog when the plane landed, but he is vague about details. He also remembers some sort of cargo, but nothing definite. He is not positive, but he thinks only the pilot took off immediately after servicing the plane.

"When we put out a 'hold' for the men, we were fifteen minutes too late.

"The United States authorities have been alerted, as well as every airport in Canada and Alaska in the event the plane shows up again. It was our bad luck not to have been alerted sooner, but the officer at Fort Norman did his best."

"I'm sure he did," Thorne said. "It was that trek in the snow that delayed me, sir." The sergeant felt a wave of thankfulness that he had not stopped for food. "Have you had any further reports?" he asked.

"All kinds of rumors," Corliss replied. "All seem to indicate that our suspects separated, and that they have disappeared without a trace."

A knock sounded at the door. Without waiting for an answer, two men entered. One was thin, small-ish, sandy-haired. He was Major Dunleigh, Commandant of the Air Force Base Hospital and Chief Medical Officer of the unit. The other, large and jolly-faced, looked keen and intelligent, with a network of laugh-wrinkles spreading from his eyes. He was Captain Lowndes, the surgeon.

Corliss wasted no time in small-talk greetings.

"Major Dunleigh, Captain Lowndes," he said. "Sergeant Thorne has come out of his coma. I would like an official diagnosis from you gentlemen, and an opinion about when he can move about. There is much to be done, and we have little time."

The captain stepped forward and felt Thorne's bandaged leg. "How are you feeling?" he asked kindly. "Leg bothering you much?"

"Fine, thank you, sir. Didn't even notice the injury until I remembered what had happened. Thanks for your good care, if you're the one to thank."

The captain smiled. "All of us helped," he said. "You and that dog of yours were bloody-looking spectacles when you were brought in. Fortunately your wounds were relatively superficial."

Corliss, standing to one side, broke in: "The report, please, Captain."

"Sorry, Inspector. Major, after you."

Dunleigh spoke in crisp, precise tones:

"The patient, from a medical point of view, was brought to this hospital suffering from shock, fatigue, and loss of blood. He was in a state of coma. He was given blood plasma, intravenous injections of saline solution to restore his metabolic balance. Thanks to amazing stamina and recuperative powers, I would say that Sergeant Thorne could be discharged and certified for active duty within twelve hours. But this is merely from my department. Captain . . ."

Lowndes smiled, lines spreading fanwise at the corners of his eyes. "From a surgical point of view," he said, "I can only add that the patient was admitted to this hospital with severe lacerations of the right leg. He also suffered from contusions on his head, but X-ray showed no fracture. His head was treated with compresses to relieve the swollen, bruised area.

"Upon first examination it was believed that leg

muscles and ligaments might be seriously damaged, but in the operating room we found only flesh lacerations due to animal bite, which had not penetrated so deeply as we supposed. The patient was treated with tetanus antitoxin and rabies vaccine. I, as surgeon, brought the open wounds together, using clamps rather than sutures. The wounds are healing with more than satisfactory speed. By tomorrow the clamps will be removed. Sergeant Thorne should be ready for duty within a few days. Before this, only if imperative. Any further questions, Inspector?"

Corliss stood silent for a moment, pondering on the information given to him. At last he spoke:

"No, nothing more, thank you. I'm grateful for the clear, accurate picture you have given me. It will help me to formulate plans. . . . And incidentally, how is the sergeant's dog—Silver Chief. That's his name, isn't it?"

Thorne leaned forward, eager to hear what progress Chief had made.

"Captain Lowndes knows more about the canine patient than I do," said the major.

"That's right," the captain said. "Since we have no veterinarian here at the Base, Silver Chief was assigned to me. And I must say he is much more intelligent than some human beings I have met. A satisfactory patient in every way. Fortunately his injury was also superficial. The bullet did not go deep. We dressed the wound and administered a stiff dose of penicillin. Except for some stiffness in the foreshoulder—which should work out with exercise —his condition is tiptop. Medically I pronounce him fit for duty."

The sergeant was vastly relieved. "Where is Silver Chief?" he asked.

"In the room next to yours," the doctor told him.

Thorne lay back relaxed, happy in the knowledge that Chief had made a good recovery. Inspector Cor-liss flashed one of his rare smiles at the other officers and said:

"Now, gentlemen, if you will excuse us, there are a few urgent official matters to be further discussed with Sergeant Thorne. It is a load off my mind to know that his health permits continuing his duties. I am very grateful to you."

"Not at all, Inspector Corliss," Dunleigh said. "As you know, we have orders to place the entire Base and all facilities at your disposal."

Again Corliss flashed a smile. "Well, then," he said, "I have another request. In about twenty minutes will you have a man sent in who can take dictation? He must be absolutely trustworthy. Sergeant Thorne will give a deposition for the trial of the man, Daroff, whom we are holding for murder."

"I know," Major Dunleigh said. "Terrible about Pilot Landry. He was popular around the Base. Anything else, Inspector?"

"Some pencils, sharp ones, please. That will be all."

"Certainly, Inspector. Don't hesitate to ask for anything you wish. It's a relief and a personal pleasure to have you here."

After Corliss nodded his thanks, Major Dunleigh saluted and preceded the captain through the door.

Thorne, who had been thinking back during this last exchange of conversation, asked suddenly:

"What happened to the half-breed, Inspector? No-kaw-i. He seemed to have been forced into this mess."

"We thought so too," the Inspector said, "and we let him go on his own recognizance. He can be reached readily, and will testify at the trial that he was bushwhacked in his own cabin."

"I see."

"Of course we're taking no chances," Inspector Corliss continued. "Though he claims no knowledge of Landry's murder, I've alerted all the surrounding posts to keep an eye on him. He has already reported however, and seems anxious to co-operate with us."

"Good. By the way, Inspector . . ."

There was a discreet knock on the door. After being asked to come in, a very smart-looking young radarman entered, pushing a typewriter on a wheeled cart. He snapped to attention and saluted Corliss.

"O'Brien, sir. I'm from Operations at Field Head-quarters. I was asked to report to Inspector Corliss, sir, of the Royal Canadian Mounted Police."

"That's me. Stand easy. Come in and shut the door."

"Yes, sir."

"Just move your machine over by the chair and have a seat. This is Sergeant Thorne." Corliss waved a hand at the patient, now propped up almost in a sitting position in his bed. "The sergeant is going to dictate testimony concerning one of your pilots. Have you got your book . . . ?"

"I take it direct, sir. I previously held a teletypist rating. You're speaking of Landry, sir? He was a good friend of mine. I would like to congratulate you, Sergeant, on bringing in the swine that did him in."

For the next hour Thorne dictated, pausing only when Corliss interrupted with shrewd, revealing questions. Finally all the events were recorded and Thorne's signature applied to the copies.

After the typist had been thanked and had wheeled his machine away, the orderly came in with tea and biscuits. As Thorne drank his tea and still crunched his biscuits, the Inspector spread out sheets of paper preparatory to taking notes.

"Now then, Thorne," he said, "just take your time. Eat and relax while you're talking. Begin from the beginning again and don't omit anything, no matter how trivial. I must impress on you again that Pilot Landry's murder is just *one* facet in this complicated business. The smallest detail might be of value."

"I understand, sir. I'll do my best."

Thorne leaned back, closed his eyes and spoke in a low, even voice . . . "And I can even remember the tea billy boiling over when Landry's position came through . . . it was 64° 58′ North by 125° 53′ West . . ."

On and on Thorne's voice continued, recalling every scrap of information he could wrest from memory. In accompaniment came the even scratching of a pencil. Silence; then Corliss wearily flung his pencil down and slowly lighted his pipe. The Inspector sat for a few minutes, staring wordlessly at the sheets before him, as if by sheer concentration he might decipher the riddle that lay somewhere beyond the written pages.

"You certainly don't deviate, Thorne," he said.
"Still, nothing is really established, though I agree
that these three foreigners must have been involved
in Landry's murder, and had some specific plan."
Thorne nodded.

"However," Inspector Corliss continued, "this is
a job for a whole field of experts. No point in our
playing guessing games. It's just a waste of time."

"Agreed," Thorne said.

"But I do have some information for you that will
come as a surprise," Corliss went on. "And it will
convince you once and for all how important this
case has become—not only to the Royal Canadian
Mounted Police, but to the Canadian Government."

Thorne sat up, alert and somewhat excited as the
Inspector took a telegram from his pocket and read:

SERGEANT THORNE WILL BE RELEASED FROM HIS
PRESENT DUTIES AND PLACED ON DETACHED DUTY PER
THIS ORDER. UPON HIS RECOVERY, HE AND HIS DOG WILL
AT THE EARLIEST POSSIBLE TIME BE FLOWN BY SPECIAL
PLANE TO OTTAWA TO AWAIT THE MINISTER OF DE-
FENSE. URGENT. ANSWER WAITED. SIGNED, SYDNEY
CROWTHER, THE OFFICE OF THE MINISTER OF DEFENSE.

Thorne whistled through his teeth. "Well—I—I!
The Minister of Defense! I surely must have run into
something big! Silver Chief to go too . . . A summons,
no less!"

"That's right, Thorne. You are very special property right now! Under a separate order we've been
instructed to keep you and your dog under twenty-
four-hour personal guard. So just because you're feel-

ing spry, don't pull any monkeyshines between now and the time you're delivered. I'm personally responsible for you both!"

Thorne grinned. "That's a pretty good one even if I say so myself. A Division Inspector responsible for a plain lowly sergeant. . . . The Minister of Defense! Well, sir, when do we leave?"

"Tonight," Inspector Corliss replied, "since the doctors believe there is no risk. So now all we are waiting for is a weather clearance from the Base Operations Office. The plane is standing by."

Thorne looked at the Inspector. "It sure looks as if you mean business, sir."

"You're right, Thorne." Then smiling, Corliss added, "Don't you think it's about time the two patients met? Silver Chief is mighty fond of you, Sergeant. He's practically asked the doctors if he could come for a visit."

Thorne sat up in bed, his face wreathed in smiles. "Let him in, Inspector."

Chapter 6

REASONS BEHIND A MURDER

THE steady drone of the engines lulled Sergeant Thorne into a reflective mood. He stared unseeing through the round, double-paned window of the Dakota transport plane. They were flying level and serene at twelve thousand feet over the wildest country on the face of the North American Continent. Much of this land had never been explored by white man or Indian; indeed, it was only since World War II that some of the territory had even been mapped. This had been done by aerial survey for the Canadian Government, but the still blanket of unbroken white beneath the plane showed no signs of light, fire or habitation.

Inspector Corliss sat huddled in his greatcoat across the aisle from Peter Thorne. He raised his head suddenly. "Sergeant," he said, "I guess I can confide to you a few minor details relating to our immediate plans."

"I wish you would," Thorne remarked.

"Since you're a key person, and the only one seen by the men we're after, secrecy is of utmost importance. We don't want those ruffians spotting you and anticipating our moves."

56

"Naturally not."

"When you leave Ottawa," Corliss continued, "it will be vital that you should not be recognized before reaching Washington, D.C."

"Washington!" Thorne exclaimed. "My mission seems to be taking on global proportions."

"That's closer to the truth than you might imagine," Corliss told him. "Anyhow—you will be in disguise. You are to impersonate a blind man . . . quite natural, since you will be using a cane for a while. And the dog will be your Seeing Eye."

Thorne laughed out loud. "Silver Chief a Seeing Eye dog!" he exclaimed.

"He'll play the part well," Inspector Corliss insisted. "We're counting on you as a team. The authorities are gathering together some civilian clothes for you and a special harness for the dog."

"Chief catches on fast," Thorne put in.

"I'm sure he does. Besides, in spite of the fact that you'll be wearing dark glasses, you will actually be doing the guiding. Think about the role for a few days, won't you? Getting used to an act makes it more natural."

"I'll do that, sir."

There was a short period of silence, as Corliss sat frowning; he seemed to be trying to figure something out. His face was still lined with perplexity when he spoke again.

"I'm almost as much in the dark about this case as you are. This much I can tell you. What has happened is part of a deep plan to defraud the Canadian Government. The plane Landry was flying was en route to Ottawa and from there to Washington with

some kind of top-secret cargo. There was a box . . .
possibly it had been hidden in that tree stump you
spoke about. I haven't been told of its contents."

"Too bad it was gone when Chief and I got there,"
Thorne said. "It must be something very important
indeed."

"Very," Corliss agreed. "It took considerable skill
and daring for the man who calls himself Daroff to
hide in Landry's plane. It also took expert timing
for the other plane to land and for the men to remove the box successfully. At least, that's apparently
what happened. It seems obvious that Daroff was
willing to lose his life, had it been necessary, to force
a crash landing."

Thorne nodded. "The other two had the same
determination. They really meant business."

"They still do," Corliss remarked. "And once more
—these men are probably just small wheels in some
large, well-trained organization. World-wide, perhaps. So you can see why I was asked to keep a
weather eye on you. After all, no one but you and
your dog are known to have made contact with the
man who stole the missing box."

Peter Thorne *was* beginning to understand! The
special protection was not just for the fun of it! True,
he had brought back one man, but others would give
much to have him silenced! The sergeant gazed out
of the window, where the stars sent a wan light down
on the moonless land. Although the cabin was com-
fortably warm, he felt a momentary chill of appre-
hension. He tried to push all thoughts of the future
aside as he closed his eyes. Now the steady drone of
the engines lulled him into fitful slumber.

Sometime later Thorne was roused by a curious honking noise. He stirred as the plane buffeted slightly and began to lose altitude. The steward approached to notify him and the Inspector that they could set their watches forward two hours. They were now in the Eastern Time Zone and would soon be passing over the vast and frozen waters of James Bay.

"Better fasten your safety belts," the steward cautioned. "That horn is a signal that the flaps are out and the wheels locked into position for landing."

About five minutes later the plane gave a jar, slight but sufficient to rouse Silver Chief, who sprang up in astonishment. They had landed, and the plane was racing down the runway after a near-perfect landing. They were now in Ottawa, the capital of Canada.

The sergeant noticed that their plane was taxiing to the far end of the apron, away from the hangars, repair shops and the commercial airport offices. In the chill predawn of Sunday morning, activity at the airport was almost at a standstill. The plane stopped beside a dark hangar where one dim, ghostly light shone through the grimy windows. There the engines spluttered and died, with a final weak cough from the exhausts. Inspector Corliss was by this time fully alert and anxious to be off.

Peter Thorne peered out of his window and saw a large, dark limousine slide out from the side of the hangar and draw up beside the exit of the plane. After the door was opened and the steps rolled into position, two shadowy figures left the automobile and ran quickly up the steps, where they held a hurried consultation with the steward.

One of them came forward into the plane, saying, "Inspector Corliss . . ."

"Here. What is it?"

"Gavin here, sir; my assistant, Filchuck over there. We are instructed to take you, Sergeant Thorne and the dog with us."

"Fine. Let's get on with it. Way past my bedtime, the sun will soon be up! Ready, Thorne?"

"Yes, sir. Come on, Chief."

Soon they were seated in the car, and the powerful limousine sped through quiet, darkened streets. Thorne noticed that the driver avoided all brightly lighted thoroughfares, seeming to skirt around the city proper.

A sharp turnoff from concrete to a rough dirt road brought Thorne to full alertness. Through the windshield he could see a pin point of light, which gradually emerged as a soft glow from a lamp shining through the window of a large house. The residence was set in the rolling countryside and surrounded by a wall of fine old fir trees.

Instead of pausing at the entrance, the driver swerved to the rear and deftly swung the car into a spacious six-door garage. He jumped out and lowered the balanced doors that had remained open for their coming. Only then did he beckon for his passengers to alight and follow him.

Thorne refused assistance as he stepped down from the car, but he felt a sharp stab of pain. He knew that his leg had become stiff from disuse during the long plane ride, but he was astonished at his weakness when he tried to hurry. He used his cane awkwardly as he hobbled over to a door where the Inspector and the other men waited. Then they all entered a dim passageway which ran directly into the house, and proceeded single file until they reached an immense, old-fashioned kitchen.

Gavin then showed the way to the library, one of the most impressive rooms Thorne had ever seen. It was beautifully proportioned, walls lined to the ceiling with books and bound documents. A huge fireplace was alight with spluttering, fragrant logs, the ruddy glow giving the room a cheery look and casting an extra sheen on the highly polished furniture. Thorne felt his spirits rise as soon as he stepped through the doorway.

A slight, well-proportioned man rose from the depths of a high wingback chair facing the fire and came around to greet his guests. His manner was warm and friendly.

"Welcome to Ottawa, gentlemen. My name is Sydney Crowther, Under Secretary to the Minister of Defense. And you must be Inspector Corliss . . ." He held out his hand.

"Right you are, Mr. Crowther. And this is Sergeant Thorne . . . Behind him, Silver Chief!"

After greeting the sergeant, the Under Secretary turned his attention to Silver Chief, "What an animal!" he exclaimed. "He looks every inch the hero we've heard so much about. I breed Labrador retrievers here, but I must say that I have never matched your dog for sheer perfection. Look at him now. He's pleased as Punch. Knows just what I'm saying about him. Don't you, fellow!"

Chief was indeed preening himself in the manner of one wholeheartedly responding to praise.

Thorne laughed. "Sure he understands. Chief is far from immune to flattery."

Mr. Crowther leaned over to make friends with the dog. In his absorption he almost forgot the visitors. Presently, though, after a vigorous tussle with the animal, the Under Secretary straightened up. "Excuse my forgetting my duties as host," he said. "You'll want to freshen up a bit. Gavin has gone for the Minister of Defense, and they'll be here shortly. Then we can have breakfast. Meanwhile I'll show you to your rooms."

After a quick wash-up, Thorne and the Inspector rejoined Mr. Crowther in the library. At that moment the library door swung open. The Under Secretary was the first on his feet to greet their visitor.

"Inspector Corliss, Sergeant Thorne, the Minister of Defense."

The man who stood before them had a keen, intelligent face, and his bearing was one of quiet authority. Smiling, he said, "It is a pleasure to see you."

After Thorne and the Inspector acknowledged this greeting, Mr. Crowther threw open the wide doors leading to the dining room. There they sat down to be served by a liveried butler, whose geniality suggested that he considered himself a second host. He too seemed to be on very friendly terms with the Minister of Defense.

"Good morning, sir," he said. "When Mr. Crowther told me you were coming, I asked Cook to prepare the eggs the way you like them."

"Good work, O'Brien," returned the Minister. "Eggs Rancheros, eh?" He turned to Thorne in explanation. "This, Sergeant, is the only place in

Canada where I can get sauce done the way they showed me when I was in Mexico a few years ago. Down there they put it on scrambled eggs, but Crowther's Nannie pours it over the individual omelet. The result is perfection!"

Thorne could not have said which part of the meal he enjoyed the most. The tea was fragrant and delicious, the buttered toast blending perfectly with wild damson jam, and the eggs worthy of the praise given them. All this fare was topped off with thick slices of browned Canadian bacon. For a short while the men ate in silence while Silver Chief lay quietly in the corner, eyes appealingly on his master.

"That dog of yours certainly has good manners," said the Minister. "Imagine his not complaining, with all this food around."

"I'll feed him shortly when I feed the Labradors," Mr. Crowther put in.

Thorne smiled his thanks.

Corliss was the first to broach the subject which was the reason for their being there. "In the midst of such good company," he said, "and after such an excellent meal, I hope I won't sound ungracious if I say it is a relief to be able to turn Sergeant Thorne over to you. No offense, Sergeant."

"I understand perfectly," Thorne told him.

"Good," Corliss returned. Then he spoke to the Minister again. "Though Thorne and his dog may be slightly the worse for wear, I got them here in one piece as requested."

The Minister smiled. "A good job too. And you may consider that your valuable cargo is now my full responsibility."

There was a brief silence as the Minister gazed down into his cup as if to find exact words for the conversation to follow. When he spoke, it was with extreme gravity. "I'm sure that you realize by now, Sergeant Thorne, that the murder of Pilot Landry is one ugly phase of a larger operation. And whereas I do not wish to tax your strength, time is of the utmost importance."

"I understand, sir. You need not concern yourself on that score. I'm feeling almost up to snuff, and the doctors agreed that I might start working any time."

"Good!" The Minister evidently accepted this statement as final. He was businesslike now as he fired questions at Thorne. "Do you know anything about physics, Thorne? Or better still, do you know anything about uranium—its ores, why it is fissionable and that sort of thing?"

"I had physics in school, of course, sir, and passed with average grades. As to uranium, I know no more than is necessary to know in connection with my duties at Fort Norman. I understand that we have a huge reactor at Chalk River, which we are using to experiment with atomic energy for commercial uses. My technical knowledge may be a little vague, from your point of view."

"In many ways this may be just as well," the Minister replied.

"I hope so," Thorne said wryly.

"I am no expert either," the Minister went on, "so I can give you only a broad outline. Later you will talk to qualified specialists to answer all questions fully."

"I see, sir."

"Meanwhile, I will go back over some matters that may sound a trifle pedantic, but which have definite bearing on our problem."

"I am very much interested," Thorne said.

"Well, if you will recall from your elemental physics, there are ninety-three metals in our world. It has taken civilization many years and untold wealth and labor to unlock the key to nature's strongbox of natural resources. For many years metals were predicted in the form of a pyramid, with some of the spaces left vacant for certain metals that should and would fall into their allotted spaces in the pyramid. Through the diligent effort of research men, along with some luck, all of the present-known metals have fallen into place. It was more or less by this method of deduction that scientists were brought on the track of uranium. Einstein said that there had to be such a metal if his equations and theories were correct. We all know now how correct they were."

"We certainly do, sir."

As the conversation seemed to be becoming a two-man affair, the Minister turned to the others. "If you two gentlemen would like to be excused," he said, "the sergeant and I can continue our talk in the library."

This was in fact a dismissal, so they all rose. Mr. Crowther motioned Silver Chief to follow him into the kitchen, but the dog would not leave until his master nodded permission, thus giving the patient animal the right to have his long-awaited breakfast. Inspector Corliss went up to his room.

When they were seated by the cheery fire, the Minister resumed his talk.

"As I said in the beginning, Sergeant, I merely want to give you a brief account of matters directly related to the present situation. You mentioned our Chalk River project—there we have what is known as a low temperature reactor. For most purposes, other than detonating a bomb or using the explosive force used in a chain reaction, atomic energy is derived from the heat it gives off. One problem is how this heat can be controlled and utilized. Do you follow me?"

"I believe so, sir."

"Well, in other words, water passing through or around pipes or condensers containing fissionable material can be made to turn into steam. This fact alone offers possibilities for unlimited military and commercial projects."

"Of course," Thorne agreed.

"But to get to the heart of the matter," the Minister continued, "we know that every nation in the world is frantically searching for a metal that can withstand the unbelievable heat necessary to contain uranium and to keep it controlled."

Thorne sat forward now, intense and alert. The Minister's voice had taken on a tone of excitement, as if the theoretical discussion had ended and was approaching some close, human reality.

"As you know, Thorne, uranium is used for the after-burner of jet and rocket planes. Another use— and probably the key to all future wars—lies in guided missiles and pilotless aircraft. The nation that can control its missiles and keep enemy planes from piercing the defensive wall will rule the world. But here again scientists have run into the problem of securing a metal that can withstand temperatures needed in the manufacture of such defensive weapons."

The Minister paused again. Resuming after a second, his eyes held a twinkle. "And don't think I am going far afield in fantasy when I say that this same problem is one of the last barriers to interplanetary travel. We think we have the fuel problem licked for rocket ships to the Moon or Mars, but no known metal or combination of metals now existing will do the trick."

Thorne smiled. "Well, at any rate," he said, "I guess we won't have to look for our fugitives on Mars."

"No," the Minister replied. "Ours is a problem very much of this world. But if we do not solve it, who can say what will happen?"

"What do you mean, sir?"

"Sergeant Thorne, the Canadian Government believes it has found this metal!"

"You mean to say, sir, that . . ."

"Exactly. I am going to leave the details to men more capable of explaining to you later the properties of this discovery. Suffice to say that one of the men in our Geological Survey Division of the Mines Department had a brilliant, yet basically simple idea. The area north and west of Great Bear Lake has an abundance of what we, both here and in the United States, believe to be the metal that will answer every requirement. Unfortunately we also know that there is an abundance of this metal in the wastelands of Russian Siberia."

"I'm beginning to put the pieces together, sir."

"Good. A month ago a very small particle of this
metal—called dikortrium, by the way—was flown to
the United States testing laboratories, for study by
members of the Atomic Energy Commission and
other scientists there. Their report confirmed every
test we had made, and told us of several other properties that this strange metal contains. Last week they
sent us a request for more, in fact quite a piece of it,
rather than just a sample. The matter was, and is,
so top secret that even your office was not alerted. We
hoped to make the delivery a routine flight, to avoid
suspicion from any quarter. Unfortunately we did
not realize how cunning and resourceful enemy
agents are, or how much they have infiltrated into the
top branches of this Government, waiting for years
for just one such opportunity to betray us and steal
for their mother country. The patience of foreign
agents is one of the most formidable weapons they
possess."

"Then you believe, sir, that Landry was murdered
by a foreign agent?"

"Precisely. But these spies will never talk, so we
are not expecting too much from this man who calls
himself Fred Daroff. After an analysis of your report
on the murder of Pilot Landry and the subsequent
fight with the two men and their dog, we are convinced they are accomplices. We have been working
backward on the case, but I will tell you in a moment
what we have run down. First I want to make clear
about dikortrium. In Landry's plane was a plain
wooden crate containing some of the ore. It was of
sound construction and, of course, there were no
markings whatever on the box. It was taken aboard

as regular stores and cargo to be flown to Vancouver. Instead, Landry was to fly due south to Washington, D.C. The rest you know. The box and its contents have completely disappeared."

"Without a trace?"

"Without a trace. But even this tells us something. The best brains in two nations are working to retrieve that box of metal ore. . . . So don't get the feeling that you are going it alone, Thorne. Your importance in this case lies in the fact that you and your dog are the only ones known to have come in contact with these men. Therefore you could readily identify them. As you must know, these agents would go to any length to prevent such identification. We cannot have you taking needless chances."

Though Peter Thorne's face was calm, he again felt a twinge of anxiety. From previous encounters with the ruthless men, he knew that there would be no hesitation to kill both himself and Silver Chief on sight.

As if reading his thoughts, the Minister broke in assuringly.

"You will have the full protection of the authorities. Your welfare is a primary consideration."

"I realize that, sir," Thorne told him.

Before continuing, the Minister leaned over to gaze thoughtfully at the flames dancing on the hearth. He spoke in tones of grave seriousness. "It is of the utmost urgency to all the free peoples of the world not to let this ore get out of the country and into the hands of Russia or her satellites. Though we and our allies desire only peace, our Intelligence reports that Russia continues feverishly to develop weapons that could give her a clear-cut advantage. Dikortrium could easily be this difference. We are fairly certain that the Russians have no inkling about the value of this ore, which lies in abundance in unexplored regions of North Siberia. We must at all costs prevent the removal of this crate from the country!"

"How do you account for the fact that they knew about the transportation of this material?" Thorne asked.

"We knew there must be a leak somewhere," the Minister returned. "Our country and the United States formed a code dealing only with dikortrium. This was to insure as much secrecy as possible. Because of the meticulous planning and execution of the theft, it was reasonable to suppose that foreign agents had inside information concerning the transportation of the box to Washington.

"We started backward for the source of possible leaks. All messages are encoded a few miles outside of Ottawa. All messages received are sent to our own office to be decoded by a cipher clerk. We would stake our lives on the reputation of the clerk employed for this purpose. He has been with the Foreign Office and on my own private staff for more than twenty years. There has been no hint of suspicion against him, nor his counterpart in the United States. Their man has been with the Department of Defense since its beginning.

"However, we have left no stone unturned and we did find a rather absurd link in our armor. Davis, our code clerk, is an elderly man living with a niece who is attending college here. To say the least, she is not the most attractive young lady in Canada, so she was very much pleased to meet a young chap Davis brought home for dinner some months ago. She took quite a fancy to this fellow, who is a telegrapher in our section.

"The potential suitor—Barthold, the name is— used to go to the Davis house two or three times a week. He learned that Davis went to bed early every night. He also found out that the old man slept very soundly. In fact, there was quite a joke about his snoring. Evidently Barthold managed to get upstairs and got hold of Davis' keys. Since it was not uncommon for the telegraphers to work different shifts, no one at the station thought it strange when Barthold came to the station around midnight and remained for two or three hours at a time. One of the weaknesses in our Government is that all the personnel have highly classified jobs and are taught not to ask questions or pry into the doings of the other clerks.

"Barthold evidently searched Davis' safe and unearthed the all-important code, along with several others. We are positive that it was through him the foreign agents were able to pin-point the departure of Landry and his plane and to plan their rendezvous.

"As to Daroff's being able to sneak aboard Landry's plane. . . . Here again we were the victims of oversimplification. We tried to arouse as little interest in the flight as possible. It would have been quite easy for Daroff to get out on the apron and to climb into the ship either before or after the crate had been secured in the plane, provided he had the nerve and ability to walk about under scrutiny. He could pretend to be doing his duty, either servicing the ship or acting as a freight handler. On the other hand, he may have crept into the rear of the fuselage the night before, when the ship was being serviced and inspected inside the hangar.

"We can't be certain about how it was accomplished, but we are sure the enemy agents knew what they were after and had a very simple and effective plan to gain their objective. In fact, it was the simplicity of their plan that insured its success."

"Almost too simple, sir."

"True, but the point is that they now have the crate and we must prevent it from falling into the hands of enemy scientists. Regaining this ore may affect the whole future of mankind. This may sound a little melodramatic, but I cannot sufficiently stress the importance of this sample of dikortrium ore."

"I understand, sir, and will do my utmost to help. As far as identification is concerned, I will never forget my assailants, nor their dog, for that matter. And I can guarantee that Silver Chief will recognize them if he ever crosses their path. I don't know if you have heard, sir, but it was Chief who saved my life when those ruffians left me unconscious in the snow."

The Minister smiled. "Yes, I heard that," he told Thorne. "And I am delighted to have the hero on my staff. As of this moment, Thorne, you are accountable only to me for your activities. . . . Now I know you must be tired. Get some rest and take the remainder of the day to loaf. Tomorrow we are putting you and your dog on the plane for Washington. There you will meet a man from the Atomic Energy Commission's most hush-hush Secret Service. Your disguise is ready for you upstairs. During the infrequent times when you are on the streets, you will assume the role already described to you. We are convinced that the Russians have agents here watching to report to well-known operatives in the United States capital. Some of the unusual activities among foreign agents all over the country are influenced, we believe, by an effort to get rid of you and Silver Chief. Go armed at all times. If necessary shoot, and shoot to kill!"

"Yes, sir."

"We have made one terrible blunder by overconfidence. Let us not make another even more tragic one."

"I will be extremely cautious, sir."

"Please do. I probably won't see you before you leave. You will make contact with Mr. Crowther or with our United States office. For Canada and myself, I wish you the best of luck in this grave undertaking; and Godspeed."

The Minister rose and held out his hand. Thorne struggled to his feet and clasped the outstretched hand.

"Thank you, sir," he said gravely. "Your confidence will not be misplaced. Not only is the matter of the missing ore to be taken care of, but also the heartless murder of Pilot Landry. He was shot in the back, sir. Never had a chance. For me, this is also unfinished business."

"Good for you, Thorne. That's the spirit I like!"

The Minister walked into the hall and, after being helped into his coat by the butler, went out to his waiting limousine.

Chapter 7

AMBUSHED

AFTER a refreshing sleep Thorne arose and started pacing around his room, his mind seething with thoughts provoked by the recent talk with the Minister of Defense. He gazed from the window onto vast gardens, now lying under a thick, uneven blanket of snow. The fine old fir trees seemed friendly, protective sentinels against an unknown future soon to be faced. As he stood there musing, a light tap sounded at the door. The sergeant smiled. He had not taken too seriously the Minister's suggestion to spend the day in rest.

"Come in," he called.

Sydney Crowther entered, carrying a brief case under his arm. He was brimming over with energy and chatter. "Well, I guess you know by now, Thorne, why the Canadian Government is taking so much interest in you!"

"I'm beginning to," the sergeant returned somewhat humorously.

"Fine. But see here, the Minister informed me that he only skimmed the surface. I have here in the brief case more reports we would like to have you study on the plane. . . . Oh, yes, your plans have been

74

changed. You are leaving for Washington later in the day. All other necessary information will be given at that end. Sure you are up to it?"

Thorne had to laugh at the question. "Would it matter?" he asked, but before Mr. Crowther had a chance to reply, the sergeant went on, "Actually I'm fine. And glad to be getting off. Too much valuable time has already been lost. It's best to get started before the trail gets too cold."

"Righto, just what we think," the Under Secretary agreed. "And I say you will get on well with your coworker in the States. He's one of the best operatives in the world."

"Good. Most of my tracking has been in the North woods, as you know. Chief and I can use the assistance of one of those smooth city chaps. But sit down. Tell me about this fellow. Mind if I pack meanwhile and get into those duds?" The sergeant indicated his disguise on a chair.

"No, go right ahead." Crowther took a seat near the window.

"Now about the man I'm to meet," Thorne prompted.

"Chap named Kincaid, a Texan. He was with the OSS during the last war and later with the FBI and Central Intelligence. He is now working with the Atomic Energy Board, so you will have at your service every facility of the United States Government as well as our own.

"I spoke with Kincaid this morning. Jack Kincaid —they call him 'Black Jack.' I explained that you are a sergeant of the Royal Canadian Mounted Police and not a Secret Service agent. He sounded delighted

at the prospect of meeting you and promises full co-
operation."

"Fine," Thorne said.

"Kincaid was especially pleased about your bringing in Daroff," Crowther went on. "He has special
reasons for not being fond of the Russians."

"Is that so? Why?"

"From the story I hear he feels that the Russians
were responsible for the death of his younger brother.
It seems that the lad was a bombardier with a B-17
outfit. They used to bomb Germany and go on over to
Russia on a shuttle if they got into trouble. When
Kincaid's brother's plane crashed in Russia the military authorities there wanted to examine it and remove valuable equipment. The Americans were
using a new secret bombsight—the new Hoving—
which was more accurate than the old Norden.
Believing it was his duty to prevent this bombsight
from falling into Russian hands, young Kincaid set
off a demolition charge that went off prematurely.
He blew himself and a couple of Russian noncoms
up. The Russians considered this a deliberate insult
to their integrity and put a bad light on the whole
affair. Subsequently the crew reported the true facts.
Young Kincaid was awarded a posthumous D.S.C., I
believe, but not until Black Jack insisted on publi-
cizing the facts."

"He doesn't sound like a chap who likes to be
pushed around," Thorne commented. "It will be a
pleasure working with him."

"I'm sure you will find it so," Crowther agreed.
"But now for a few last-minute details, then you'll

be on your own. First, you are to be transported on a commercial airline. You will be known by the code name 'Orange.' Kincaid is 'Black.' " Crowther reached into the brief case and brought out a packet which he handed to the sergeant. "Here is plenty of money," he said, "American and Canadian. If there is anything else you need, either wire or phone to my office, using your code name. I will be in constant communication with the Minister of Defense."

A few hours later, Peter Thorne, dressed in mufti, arrived by taxi with Silver Chief at the Ottawa airport. Thorne wore his dark glasses and managed his cane with the gait of a blind man. Silver Chief, however, could not accustom himself to the leather harness, and kept trying to shake himself loose from the outlandish contraption into which he had been strapped. He had, upon occasions, been hooked up to a dog sled, but never had he been under the restriction of any harness such as the one he was now wearing. Had it not been for his master's calming voice, Chief would have tried to snap off his barrier against freedom.

A cold, wintry sunset was falling over the city of Washington as the plane bearing Thorne glided into National Airport. Thorne could see the lighted Capitol dome, the Washington Monument, stark and needlelike as it pierced the heavens, and other landmarks familiar from his boyhood history books. The thought that he had come well over three thousand miles in twenty-four hours, and could, if need be, be in two of the great capitals of the world the same

day gave him a much greater thrill than he was prepared to admit.

The plane taxied up to the commercial airline
ramp past workshop hangars and the restricted area
reserved for MATS, the Military Air Transport System, that flew men and cargo to the far corners of
the earth for the three Armed Services. There it
stopped. Steps were rolled up, and the door of the
plane thrown open. Passengers moved out into the
gathering darkness at National Airport.

Silver Chief stepped gingerly out onto the steps
that led to the ground, his stiff blind-man's harness
apparently leading Thorne, though in reality it was
Thorne who controlled the dog. When they reached
the bottom step and were about to walk over to the
airport with the rest of the passengers, Thorne felt
a strong hand grasp his elbow and steer him into
the darkness between two hangars. Silver Chief
stopped, turning to see what had changed their direction. A strange man was speaking to his master in
low and urgent tones.

"Are you color-blind?" the stranger asked.

"Yes," Thorne replied. "I cannot distinguish the
color Orange."

"Curious, I have the same trouble with Black.
This mutual affliction must mean we're supposed to
work together. Come along, Sergeant. I have a car
waiting. Your bags will be brought over later."

Without a word, Thorne allowed himself to be led
to a small, inconspicuous coupe, its lights out, parked
in the shadows of the hangar. As they later drove
toward clusters and rows of lights dotting the city,
Thorne tried to study the man beside him without

appearing too obvious. Through his tinted glasses Kincaid's strong profile stood out boldly. As they neared the end of the Potomac Bridge, the driver turned a little, speaking suddenly.

"O.K., Thorne. You can take those goggles off for a while." When they had crossed the river, the car swerved up to the curb to be parked in shadows of the Mall. "Jack Kincaid, here. Pausing to give you an official greeting!"

The men shook hands. Thorne could feel the warm cordiality in his new co-worker's clasp. Then Kincaid took time to notice Silver Chief.

"So you're the dog I've heard so much about! How are you, old man? Boy, you're some hound! Bigger and tougher than I expected." Kincaid leaned over to rumple the hair on Silver Chief's head and ears. The feel and smell and talk of this strange person must have pleased the dog, for he gave a few short, friendly barks and then performed the best tail-wagging possible in such close quarters.

Kincaid's attitude toward the dog drew Thorne even closer to him. The sergeant now studied more carefully this American, whose vitality gave an impression of harnessed, concentrated power. And though Thorne realized at a glance that he and Kincaid were temperamentally unlike, he felt certain that they shared many beliefs in common. In looks they were very different. Kincaid was the taller by about three inches, and lean and muscled as a whip snake. Then, too, Kincaid's hair was very dark, his blue-black whiskers showed through his fair skin, though he was closely shaven. The sergeant was glad to have this man on his side instead of against him.

for there seemed to be a ruthless directness about the Texan that he had seldom encountered.

Yet at this moment of their meeting, Thorne trusted the man, and he was pleased that Chief was also drawn to him. His dog's attachments had always proved well founded. The sergeant could not help thinking how little difference in nationality and temperament mattered when men shared the same ideals.

After a few more conventional phrases of welcome, Kincaid started the car again and became very businesslike.

"I guess it must seem odd to you, Sergeant, that we dragged you down here and away from the job you know so well . . ."

"I had wondered if I might not have been more useful close to the scene of murder," Thorne admitted. "This would certainly be true if the culprits were still in Canada."

"No doubt about that," Kincaid returned. "You might even say that we're not absolutely certain whether some of them are not still up there. When we lost track of the two men at Dawson City, that was our last tangible clue. From then on we've been working on a general theory about the way such men operate—plus a few indications."

"They could not get anything out of Daroff then?"

"Nothing. He hasn't said a word in his own defense or admitted any connection with the others. It's pretty obvious, though, that he is Russian or of Russian descent; also, it is logical to assume that Russia would be the world power most interested in securing a sample of the ore and using it for her own advantage. Though this is not an established fact, there are the indications I mentioned before."

"Such as . . . ?"

"Well, for the past few days there has been furious activity on the phones, radio broadcasts and diplomatic wires of the Russian Embassy here in Washington. Of course, this is the central point for all foreign agents in the country. The Russians are using a new code that we haven't been able to crack yet."

"Have the messages taken on any kind of pattern?" Thorne asked.

"Only that most of the activity centers between here and San Francisco, and since that city is such a likely point of departure, we are convinced that the thieves are headed there. You might say that these are *intangible* clues, but they are something to go on. At any rate, we felt them important enough to have you here and available, instead of tracking in the wilds of Canada."

"I can see your point," Thorne said.

Kincaid laughed. "You still sound a little doubtful. But tomorrow one of my men will show you how the FBI takes intangible clues and converts them into usable facts. Then you'll be thoroughly convinced."

"I'll be very much interested to see the FBI in action," Thorne told him.

"Fine. Now as to our immediate plans. You are already registered in a nice family-type hotel—the Middlesex Arms. Very agreeable management. No objections to Silver Chief. I have the next room, though we're presumably not together. For your pro-

tection I have requested the management to see that
the adjoining door remains unlocked."

"I see," Thorne said.

"I hope you can see just as clearly that the Russians
would stop at nothing to get you out of the way,"
Kincaid warned. "Even *they* have agents who will
talk for money—and it has been reliably reported
that your name is a key topic with the underground
even here in Washington."

"Nothing like being in the spotlight," Thorne said
grimly. "By the way, have you picked up the chap
who decoded those dikortrium messages from
Canada?"

"Not yet. He's probably lying low, knowing that
the search is on."

Kincaid's small coupe was now moving at a jerky,
erratic speed through a heavily trafficked street.
Thorne had a feeling that they were nearing their
destination.

"I hope there's no special business tonight," he
said. "Frankly, I could do with a bit of sleep."

"Nothing tonight," Kincaid said, as he took one
hand from the steering wheel and fumbled in his
pocket. "Here's your key, Thorne. We will not be
going in together. On with the goggles and keep up
the disguise every minute.

"Tomorrow morning you will be picked up by one
of my men, who will serve both as guide and body-
guard. When you have finished with what we want
you to see, return to your room. I will contact you
personally."

"Right."

"I don't imagine you will be gone very long. But

we are going about this search as scientifically as we
know how, and you'll have to be briefed on certain
matters before we can proceed. Meanwhile, all assem-
bled data are being put through our electric IBM
machines. I'll have information concerning it on file
by the afternoon. Then we're off on a short trip for
the study of another little problem, and the search
begins in earnest. So you see, Thorne, we have the
resources of two nations at our service."

"That's good to know, Kincaid," the sergeant said.

After they were settled in Room 610, Thorne
slipped the heavy harness from his dog, but he waited
to remove his own disguise until he had finished the
food Kincaid had ordered for him. When the waiter
removed the table, Thorne told him that he did not
wish to be disturbed any more that night. The man
said that he would tell them so at the desk, using the
usual polite, gentle tones in which most people address the blind.

A blanket had been placed in a box on the floor for
Silver Chief, who immediately made himself at home,
with no fuss about the strange surroundings. The
sergeant was so tired he scarcely remembered getting
into bed and falling into a sound, unbroken sleep.

At ten-thirty the next morning Thorne and Silver
Chief moved through the lobby, the sergeant adopt-
ing the unsure gait of a blind man, with Silver Chief
back in his harness. A small coupe like the one Kincaid had driven the night before was parked at the
hotel entrance. The sergeant stood like a man unde-
cided, until the driver jumped out and solicitously
helped Thorne and his dog into the waiting car.
Immediately the man at the wheel pulled away from

the curb to join a stream of traffic headed for downtown Washington.

"I'm Brooks, Central Intelligence," the young agent said. "Hope you enjoyed your breakfast, sir. Washington is known for its fresh orange juice."

"I had my oranges sliced," Thorne told him. "Where are we headed, Brooks?"

"Black asked me to take you to the FBI Building," Brooks replied.

For a while they drove in silence, Chief seated beside his master, ears cocked forward, his shiny wet nose sampling the strange city odors. Thorne marveled at the crisp, cold winter's day, with a sun so brilliant that it warmed the air. He was equally impressed with the uniform order and cleanliness of the thoroughfares. Thorne mentioned this to Brooks as the young agent parked the car.

"How do they manage to keep the city so clean?" the sergeant asked.

"It's very simple, Sergeant. Washington has only one excuse for being, namely, government. That's about all the industry we have around here. No factory smoke, no grime and very little litter. It is big business all right, but not the kind that produces soot."

Looking down Constitutional Avenue at the mile upon mile of Government office buildings, Thorne had to admit the bigness of Government business. Nor did he change his mind during the tour of the FBI headquarters, where he was given a methodical briefing of various departments. At each door he was told the contents of the room before entering.

All the divisions of highly specialized crime detection, which is the primary function of the Federal Bureau of Investigation, were represented.

The FBI gathers the evidence of crime and then makes it available to whichever bureau or agency of the Federal Government is acting as the accuser. Mistakenly enough, however, many people feel that the FBI prosecutes its cases. On the contrary, the FBI is an investigation agency only, housed in its own building, a huge, well-organized laboratory, where every branch of science and criminology is used in the complex art of crime detection.

Brooks showed Thorne the eighty million fingerprints on file, explaining telltale features and positive identification; also the batteries of teletype machines that flash the information to agents all over the United States and the world.

Sergeant Thorne, with the ever-eager Silver Chief at his side, was impressed with the enormity and complexity of the behind the scenes activity which Brooks explained continued twenty-four hours a day, three hundred and sixty-five days a year.

"There are no holidays in the war against crime," he said.

After the sergeant had been shown all that had been planned for that visit to the FBI headquarters, he and Brooks returned to the car. As they drove at a leisurely pace toward the Middlesex Arms, Brooks co-ordinated all they had seen with practical application to the problem at hand.

"You can begin to see now, Sergeant, how much leg work and hunting-a-needle-in-the-haystack method our machines save. Your report, which had been forwarded by Inspector Corliss, was gone over minutely for anything that might identify the men we're after. For instance, I believe you mentioned that the larger man wore glasses and that one of his eyes was crossed."

"That's correct, his left eye."

"Well, we immediately checked our cards of all subversives and criminals wearing glasses, and those who were judged to be logical suspects in this sort of case. The next step was to narrow it down to those having crossed eyes—then left crossed eyes and so on. By a process of elimination, we were actually able to reduce thousands of cards to some twenty or thirty suspects with the characteristics you described."

"In other words," the sergeant interrupted, "if anything dramatic comes from your study it will save time for us . . ."

"Exactly. If we unearth anything, the information will go out on teletype to the nearest agent, who will have the groundwork done before you and Jack Kincaid even arrive on the scene. It's all routine and not very romantic, but it pays off, believe me!"

Thorne could not help smiling at the young man's sincerity and enthusiasm. "I'm sure it pays off," he agreed. "The FBI is known all over the world for startling results."

"Thanks for the kind words, Sergeant. We've heard about the Royal Mounted down here too!"

As they drove up to the curb in front of the hotel Brooks had a final bit of advice, which he delivered softly to Thorne.

"Black told me to say that you'd be moving along pretty fast now. You are to go to your room and wait for him. He might even be there now. . . . It's certainly been a pleasure meeting you, Sergeant."

"Same here. And thanks for the tour."

Thorne allowed himself to be led into the hotel by Silver Chief and then over to the elevator. While waiting for it to come down he glanced about. The desk clerks were busy sorting mail, and no other person could be seen in the small, cozy-looking lobby. Hurriedly he crossed to the newsstand and bought a paper, arriving back at the elevator before the door had opened to discharge a few guests. Man and dog entered and were swiftly delivered to the sixth floor.

Silver Chief, sensing that he would be released from his heavy leather harness as soon as they reached the room, tugged Thorne along with such force that he was almost trotting down the corridor behind his powerful dog.

"Some Seeing Eye you are," the sergeant grumbled. "Good thing the hall is deserted!"

As they came to a turn in the corridor, Thorne reached into his pocket for a key, just as they were passing an alcove containing a hydrant and a coiled fire hose. Suddenly Silver Chief whirled about, his fangs bared in a snarl of hatred and surprise. This violent yanking probably saved Thorne's life, for it threw him off balance. Thus the knife of an assailant, descending upon Thorne and cutting his coat as if it were no more than soft cheese, merely grazed the sergeant's flesh.

Thorne whirled to face his would-be murderer.

He was too late. The man, coattails flying, was headed
toward the fire-escape door at the end of the corridor.
Chief sped with vengeance, but his heavy harness
hampered him as he chased behind the man, now

crying in terror at the snarling animal. Chief made
a desperate leap as they reached the door, but, thrown
off balance by the harness, his snapping teeth closed
only on a mouthful of coat.

By this time the sergeant had his revolver out and
he shouted for the man to stop. The command was

ignored, as the stranger kicked free and tried to bash Chief's head as he opened the fire-tower door. Thorne fired, but the man managed to get through. Meanwhile, Chief stood frantically scratching on the

wood, while still retaining the piece of cloth in his huge jaws.

The shooting in the corridor made all bedlam break loose. Doors popped open, heads were thrust out and women's screams sounded up and down the halls.

Chapter 8

ESCAPE

Y THE time Thorne managed to get the fire-
tower door open, his assailant had disappeared
down a turn on the concrete stairs.

"After him, Silver Chief. Don't let him get away!"
Thorne shouted.

The sergeant felt drops of blood oozing down over
his chest. Pain from the cut was slight and would not
have prevented his pursuit of the culprit, but Thorne
realized he could make little time because of his injured leg. Turning toward the elevator, he ran head-
on into Kincaid, who was holding a revolver in his
hand.

"You all right?" Jack gasped.

Thorne nodded and reached over to recover the
piece of material that had been torn from the attacker's coat.

"Which way did he go?" Kincaid asked.

Thorne pointed to the door, and his friend was
halfway through when he shouted back:

"Meet you downstairs. Take the elevator."

Meanwhile, Silver Chief raced down the six flights
of stairs as fast as he could, pausing at each floor to
sniff at doors leading to the corridors. The scent

continued down and down, and as Chief trotted
through the basement hall, he knew that the enemy
was close by. After bounding up five short steps, the
dog found himself among a litter of trash barrels and
garbage cans. For a moment he lost the direct scent,
but he picked it up again just in time to see a man
dash toward a waiting limousine. Chief sprinted,
bracing himself to a stop just as the fugitive flung
himself into the car and slammed the door. Though
the dog leaped high, a pane of glass separated him
from the person who had attacked his master!

Chief barked ferociously, hoping that the sergeant
would appear; but it was Jack Kincaid who came
dashing up the basement steps just in time to see the
large blue limousine back down the alley and onto
Dupont Circle. Kincaid grasped Silver Chief's harness and hustled him through the rear door and into
the hotel lobby, just in time to see Thorne burst out
of the elevator. The three then hurried to Kincaid's
car, which was parked on the hotel lot. In a flash the
small coupe was roaring in pursuit.

"We might be able to catch him yet," Kincaid
muttered. "This after-lunch traffic will slow big cars
down."

Completely at ease and with breath-taking skill,
he maneuvered the small machine in and out between the larger, more cumbersome vehicles. Slowly
they gained on the car ahead. With a squeal of
brakes the limousine turned right and sped toward
the outskirts of the city.

"I think I know where he is headed," Kincaid said.
"Switch on my radio."

For another ten blocks the two cars sped through

the Washington traffic, while Kincaid managed to keep within a block of his quarry. Without warning, and at full speed, the big blue limousine turned left, and swerving on two wheels, raced through a massive pair of iron grillwork gates. Thorne caught a glimpse of the driver's face as he turned to look at his pursuers. The car disappeared into the grounds behind the gates. Jack yanked on his emergency brake. He was still muttering under his breath as the little coupe skidded to a halt against the curb.

"I knew it! What did I tell you, Thorne?"

Thorne was completely baffled. "I don't know what you are talking about, Jack."

"You'll see what I mean," Jack answered. "That's the Russian Embassy Building. Even if that man had killed you, he could claim diplomatic immunity by proving he was attached to the diplomatic corps of the Embassy.

"Of course, it's a joke, and we all know it," Jack went on, "for the Russians abuse this privilege wherever they are. Every agent working for them carries a diplomatic visa. It would take weeks of red tape and phone calls to get that man out from under their protective wing."

"I know about their diplomatic immunity, Kincaid; they pulled the same stunt up in Canada. It seems incredible that they can get away with it."

Jack Kincaid did not even bother to answer as he reached for his radio microphone.

"Hello, hello! Black Jack speaking. I have along an orange crate. Location—outside the Russian Embassy. I want ten of our best men down here pronto. Everyone entering and leaving the Embassy is to be shadowed, including the Ambassador. Special watch for a man as follows . . ." Here he handed the mike to Thorne, "Sketch in roughly the man who attacked you."

Thorne described his assailant as well as he could from the quick look he had gotten of him, then Kincaid took over again. "We have a piece of material that I am bringing to Headquarters for analysis as soon as reinforcements arrive here to take over. That is all. Over and out."

Kincaid was silent for a while, the frown on his forehead producing an angry, puzzled expression. "Was this man one of those who attacked you at Fort Norman?" he asked.

"Definitely not. He had not the slightest resemblance to either of them."

"Strange. Very strange."

Then Jack lapsed into silence again.

After about ten minutes Kincaid briskly straightened up. He seemed to have been alerted to something yet invisible to Thorne. After glancing hurriedly about, Jack started up the motor.

"Have your men come already?" Thorne exclaimed.

"Yes, and they have taken up their posts. Remember what I said on the radio. I wanted *ten* of our *best* men—and I have them. We're not playing games and believe me no one will leave the Embassy without being shadowed and their descriptions handed in. As for us, we may as well be off."

As they drove toward FBI Headquarters Kincaid again seemed abstracted and far away. He asked Thorne to wait in the car while he took the material

inside for analysis. Returning promptly, he jumped
into the car.

"O.K., Thorne, let's get back to the hotel and get
that cut of yours fixed up."

The sergeant nodded.

"What I've been trying to figure," Jack went on,
"is how those agents got a line on your disguise so
fast."

"They certainly didn't waste any time," Thorne
agreed.

They drew up to the hotel then, and after going
upstairs the sergeant went into the bathroom,
stripped off his shirt and treated the long, superficial
cut across his neck and shoulders.

"Need any help, Pete?" Kincaid asked. When the
sergeant said that he was making out all right, Jack
continued grumbling to himself, "You might as well
forget that disguise for all the good it did. And you,
too, Chief. The Seeing Eye stuff did not work at
all . . ."

Kincaid leaned down to unfasten the heavy harness, and the dog, realizing that he was being released
from a role he had never cared for, yelped short barks
of delight. He then rolled over and over on the floor
with delight at being able to scratch his back against
the carpet.

As if he had also been figuring, Thorne called from
the bathroom, continuing their talk. "Maybe one of
their agents in Ottawa spotted me," he said.

"Could be, but I don't believe it. There was so
little time to have followed you up there. Anyhow,
the Russians must have agents all over the place to
have caught on so soon. Look—now tell me every-

thing that took place since you left Brooks. I know the visit to Headquarters went off all right. What happened *after* you left him?"

"I came into the hotel. Silver Chief towed me directly to the elevator. While waiting there I looked around and since nobody was in sight I went over to the newsstand and bought a paper. But I was back at the elevator before it came down and discharged passengers."

"You bought what!"

Thorne, who was looking at himself in the bathroom mirror, could see his face turn beet-red from embarrassment. He needed no explanation to remind him of his folly, but one was freely and sarcastically given.

"A blind man buying a newspaper! Really, Thorne. Why not just hang a sign on yourself saying, I'm a phony!"

The sergeant was too humiliated to reply. He buttoned on a fresh shirt in silence, and neither was there a sound from the other room. Presently it was Kincaid who broke the strain.

"Well, that's water under the dam," he said. "Pack up, will you? We've got a three o'clock appointment with a man from the Atomic Energy Commission. Not much time to get to Virginia."

Chapter 9

CONTENTS OF THE BOX

JACK KINCAID's little coupe sped along the ribbon of concrete with the purr of an expensive limousine. Few words passed between the men as the miles slipped behind them. Sergeant Thorne still smarted from the criticism of his partner, all the more because the blame had been merited. Exposing his presence in Washington had been a serious blunder . . . And he'd been so anxious for Jack to think well of him! As if in answer to the sergeant's self-blame, Kincaid spoke.

"Buck up, Thorne," he said. "We all make mistakes. I'm sure I would muff the ball if I were in your territory. Naturally our techniques are different. We aren't dealing with fur robberies or land grants now —the gang we're after want to dominate and control the world. They play for keeps. And look, Pete, if I let you have it, it was because revealing yourself could mean your end."

Jack's anxious tones completely mollified the sergeant. "Your criticism was absolutely justified," Thorne replied. "But believe me when I say that I *do* realize the seriousness of our situation. After all, I have personally tangled with these characters."

"I know that, so let's forget the matter, and let me tell you where we are going and why."

"I wish you would," the sergeant told him.

"We'll begin with this dikortrium stuff," Kincaid said. "You know it is very tricky. Actually I know practically nothing about it myself. That is why we're down here. My chief claims that knowing a few details about the ore might help us considerably in our search."

"Our trip would be worth-while if this is so," Thorne said. "But why in Virginia? Couldn't we have gotten the same information in Washington?"

Kincaid shook his head. "Evidently you don't realize that the Atomic Energy Commission, along with the Armed Services, has a duplicate setup down here, including all of the facilities of our Washington offices. They are both run on a skeleton staff."

"Why the duplication and extra expenses?" the sergeant asked.

"Security. Here we have stores of microfilm records of what is going on in Washington. Just in case . . ."

"I see. A sneak attack or an atomic explosion over Washington?"

"Right. Anyhow, this ore we're concerned about is so top secret I don't believe there are a dozen people in the world who know about it. One of them, a nuclear scientist, is stationed here. His only duties are to inquire into the properties of DK and to test it. He is responsible to no one, unless there is something special to report. It is safer and more isolated here than any spot in a large city could be. We are on our way to see him to get some firsthand data. No more telephones, cables or coded messages."

"Good," said Thorne. "It will be interesting to get scientific information from an expert."

"I agree. Meanwhile, that torn piece of cloth from the coat of your assailant is being put through the tests. By the time we get back we'll have a report on that. We have already uncovered some facts that will amaze you."

As Kincaid spoke, he swung the car sharply to the right, onto a concrete road only half as wide as the highway they had just left. Before them lay a low chain of hills, gently rising above the countryside, bare and stark in the winter afternoon. Thorne noticed that the scattered barns and houses dotting the landscape seemed strangely without life. Neither cattle nor people nor any sign of life was visible about the farms.

"I see you are examining the terrain," Kincaid said. "Everything within a two-mile radius is controlled by the Atomic Energy Commission. No one is allowed on the grounds without proper credentials. The guards at the fence towers can see for five hundred yards in any direction. We are also being scanned on radarscope this very minute. This is one place they don't take any chances. Even the President of the United States has to produce a proper pass of identification to get through these gates."

The coupe drove up to an imposing, double-gated tower that had the appearance of a fortress. Armed guards patrolled the upper level; below, two others stepped out from small enclosures and approached the car. Thorne could see men staring from within, their Tommy guns alerted—not just casually held as a routine act.

The inspection was brief but thorough. Kincaid showed two passes and explained that Silver Chief was included on Thorne's pass. At first the guard was hesitant to allow a dog into the premises, but after examining the signature he waved the car through.

After leaving the coupe on a concrete-covered parking lot, the two men and Silver Chief walked to a rise of earth planted to simulate the surrounding countryside. A small door set in this hillock was opened by remote control. Clearly the two investigating officers were being watched from some unseen point at all times. They entered a huge, brightly lighted tunnel. Doors lined both sides, each one labeled with a series of coded numbers and letters. The subdued hum of powerful machines at work throbbed through the corridors. Thorne felt as if he had entered a temple devoted to the god of energy. The explosion of the atom—the smallest and most powerful force ever harnessed by mankind and all its secrets for good and destruction lay within this vast and busy cave. Even Silver Chief seemed to feel tension in the atmosphere, for he moved hesitantly.

Kincaid turned at one of the doors and pushed a button. Instantly the door swung open. For the second time they were faced by an armed guard who demanded to see their papers. Kincaid patiently explained about Silver Chief, and they were admitted into a well-appointed office. A door stood ajar, and Thorne could see into a laboratory crammed with test tubes, and tables covered with scientific instruments. Again he could hear the low, powerful hum of motors. Before they had time to sit down, a man emerged from the lab, unfastening his white laboratory gown as he approached. He recognized Kincaid and walked over to shake hands.

"Kincaid. Good to see you again. Washington told me to expect you. And this . . . " He turned questioningly toward Thorne.

Kincaid introduced the two. "Professor, this is Sergeant Thorne of the Royal Canadian Mounted Police. Thorne, Professor Cronkite. And incidentally, Professor, that's Silver Chief, the sergeant's dog. Isn't he a beauty?"

"Glad to know you, Thorne. Please have a seat. That certainly is some animal you have there. Does he bite?"

"Only the wrong people, sir. Don't worry about him."

"Sit down, gentlemen. As you can see, we are all pretty busy around here. I understand that I am to give you certain details of dikortrium, in the hope that you will be able to identify the stolen crate and its contents."

"Right, sir."

The professor continued musing to himself just as if he had not heard Thorne's reply.

"Most amazing properties. Do either of you know anything at all about it?"

Kincaid shook his head, and Thorne answered for them both.

"Very little, sir. The Minister of Defense in Ottawa spoke briefly about the ore. But, as he said himself, even he knows very little about it."

"Well, here goes then." The tall, angular professor lighted an oversized stove match and placed it to an enormous, smelly pipe, drawing in until a cloud of smoke filled the air. "In the first place, dikortrium, which we call DK, is *literally* out of this world. This is one of the reasons why it is so important. I did not mean to make a bad pun at your expense, but DK is a metal from the universe itself."

"What?" Kincaid and Thorne simultaneously expressed their surprise.

"Exactly. DK comes to this planet from the universe about us. As you probably know, the sun is a boiling mass of molten metal and solids that we have not been quite able to analyze through our spectroscopes. However, we do know that its center is bubbling away at the unbelievable temperature of one million degrees, and is constantly spewing out huge chunks of molten metal into the universe.

"The same sort of thing occurs from several other planets in our universe; for instance, Saturn, which we now believe to be in a semiliquefied state. The rings, which we once believed to be cloud formations, we now think are gaseous rings formed by the eruption and throwing off of millions upon millions of small meteors from the main molten mass of the planet itself.

"However, to get on. A considerable number of these meteors that are hurled out into space from their mother planet are many times the size of this earth; some are smaller. As they hurtle, escaping the orbit of their mother planet, they occasionally collide. Sometimes they merely flow along in an almost liquid state through the incalculable cold of outer space.

"As you both know, there are millions of these meteors flying through space from every direction—

even from the farthermost reaches of the universe. In fact, it is these uncharted, unknown, and completely unpredictable meteors that are the chief hazard to interplanetary travel today.

"Almost every *technical* problem which we have run into has been licked, or is in process of being overcome. But no one—absolutely no one—has been able to discover a solution to the problem of uncharted meteors that might be encountered in space travel.

"I don't mean to get off the track. The problem I have just mentioned is of no concern to us here; it is just a little story leading up to our problem. Interested?"

Both men nodded vigorously.

"As these meteors fly through the uncharted waste of the heavens, some are caught in the gravitational pull of the planet earth. At this point they become of special interest to us. When these meteors hit our belt of air in the stratosphere, going thousands of miles an hour, the friction that sets in and the heat generated is almost unbelievable. These are the shooting stars you see on any clear night hurtling across the heavens. Sometimes you can see three and four at the same time. There is nothing extraordinary about this phenomenon. It happens all over the world many hundreds of times a day. Nine hundred and ninety-nine thousand times out of a million, the meteor cannot withstand the heat it has generated and merely burns itself out into ash before it ever comes within harmful distance of the earth.

"There are several accurate descriptions in history,

however, of huge meteors shooting through earth's barrier of air and striking the earth with such force is to affect the destiny of whole nations profoundly. One such theory often is used to explain the Deluge, or Flood, that occurred in Biblical times. There have been others."

During this talk, Silver Chief lay curled up half asleep, one ear cocked toward the professor, the other twitching at an occasional nonexistent fly.

Thorne and Kincaid sat spellbound as the professor, now and again inhaling huge puffs of smoke, went on.

"For some reason, which we have not even been able to answer—even in theory—an area slightly north and east of your Canadian Great Bear Lake, and an equally vast and uninhabited area of Siberia, centering around Lake Baikal, seem to be where most of the meteorites or aerolites do crash when they survive the friction of earth's atmosphere. We are not here to theorize, but what I have just told you has been well-known to every scientist in every country of the world for some time.

"So now we have arrived at the fact," he continued, "that one of two major concentrations of these falling meteors is in our hands, and an equally, if not larger, and more productive area of meteorites lies securely within Russian hands.

"But here is the difference, gentlemen." The professor chuckled. "Here is the difference. We know about meteorites and what a wonderful new treasure they are. We believe that Russia has no inkling of her undiscovered wealth. That is why that crate with the sample of DK must never reach Russia. Scientists there are quick to learn and profit from others who have led the way in discovery and research.

"And now to DK itself and its importance to us. As you well know, both the United States and Canada, as well as every other nation on earth, are conducting a vast search for uranium deposits.

"Either by luck or by brilliant deductive theory, one of your Canadian geophysicists came upon a small meteorite and decided to run some tests for himself. Imagine his surprise when no known method made the slightest impression on the baseball-size chunk of metal he was trying to break down and analyze.

"He immediately dug up another small chunk and sent it to Chalk River, explaining that no heating process he possessed could melt, much less scorch, his new discovery. The sample was put through the reactor chambers at Chalk River. The results may well change the balance of world power for generations to come.

"The report was flashed to us that Chalk River was in possession of a metal that melted somewhere between one hundred and sixty and one hundred and eighty-five thousand degrees!

"This, gentlemen, was the missing link in the plans for rocket flight, for guided missiles, for everything needs to go through the severe strain of supersonic flight and still retain its form and strength. The research laboratories of every Government in the world have made this Project A in their plans. The search for a metal with these properties is considered even more important than finding uranium ore.

"Unfortunately, Chalk River had made the sample radioactive in the process of melting it, so we in the United States were sent the original sample for tests. Can you imagine a metal that can withstand the heat of one hundred thousand blowtorches turned on it, and not even show a singed hair, so to speak? It was uncanny.

"Meanwhile, your man up in Fort Norman went off into the wilderness to collect some more samples. I was assigned to put his original find through every known test. Some of the results are so stupendous I cannot believe them myself. I received several more samples from Canada, but they varied in quality from the original two samples. From spectrographic analysis I have deduced the theory that the stuff we want must be a throwoff from the sun, not from any other planet.

"This, I believe, because in the sample I have seen are contained *all* the metals and organic compounds that we on earth are familiar with. There are also other alloys or series of alloys in the metal that defy analysis. These are the key to uniting and fusing these crashed meteorites into a mass that can withstand temperatures necessary to pierce the earth's atmospheric barrier.

"One of the absolute tests to identify the meteorites we want—quite simple if you have the key to it —I discovered by accident. But by using this simple but infallible test, our man in Canada can spot the correct type of meteorite in seconds. And this is where you two come in, and I am now divulging one of our most closely guarded secrets. In fact, only one other person knows what I am about to tell you,

Gilchrist, the man up in Fort Norman. If he and I were to die, our secret would die with us, as neither of us ever wrote it down.

"Gentlemen, DK, among its many other properties, emits ultraviolet as well as infrared rays! I have here some specially prepared glass, which I want you to look through. Look at me. Take a peek in the lab and tell me what you see."

Professor Cronkite opened his desk drawer and solemnly handed each man a small monoclelike piece of thick tinted glass. Both men held the glass to an eye, and both gasped at the same time.

"Kincaid! Do you see it? His hand . . . The lab . . . Look in there?"

The dark-haired Texan was overwhelmed. "Holy smoke. Look at that, Thorne . . . Green . . . See his hands . . . Bright green!"

Cronkite seemed pleased at their amazement.

"Exactly, gentlemen. With a piece of that glass you or anyone else can spot dikortrium fifty feet away. Everything DK touches retains minute particles of infrared and ultraviolet rays which it emits, much like radioactive uranium. It is not harmful, but it certainly has made your task easier. Although the men who stole that large sample that was being shipped here might have the fanciest alibi in the world, nothing on earth can rid them of the color after coming in contact with the material, until it wears off from natural friction and time.

"So there you have it: dikortrium in the afterburners of jet planes, in atomic cannons, in hundreds of peaceful and warlike uses, will be able to change the face of the earth when brought under control.

It is malleable and contains all the desirable properties of *all* metals of our earth plus two or three I
know nothing about, from our mother, the sun itself
—the giver of life on this planet. Let us make sure
that it is not used as the destroyer of life on earth,
for in the wrong hands this metal has that power."

Thorne and Kincaid were so awed by the professor's solemn words that they could not speak. Carefully each put his glass-piece in a pocket.

Cronkite broke the silence.

"Well, that's it. The rest is up to you. I can only
hope and pray that the crate has not gotten away from
us. If you should break the glass, send us a wire at
our Washington Headquarters at once. But *don't
lose it!* You see what I mean, I'm sure. Good luck to
you both. And now if you will excuse me."

The professor rose to end the discussion. Kincaid
led the way to the door, too absorbed in his thoughts
even to say good-by, Thorne and Silver Chief following, after a brief nod toward the man upon whom
so much responsibility rested.

A young secretary in the outer office who held a
phone receiver to his ear stopped Kincaid, beckoned
him to take it.

"Your office has been holding this line open for
ten minutes, Mr. Kincaid. They said it was urgent.
I'm not allowed in Professor Cronkite's office. Will
you explain this?"

"Sure. Thanks." Kincaid spoke abruptly into the
mouthpiece.

"Kincaid speaking. Okay, Mac. Sorry to hold you
up. Rules are rules down here. WHAT! Really . . ."
A slow grin spread across his face.

Thorne could hear the crackle of terse conversation coming over the wire. "Great. We'll be there in thirty minutes. Get it set up at Bolling Field with the Air Force, Mac. Tell them this is DK emergency. We've finished here. Can't talk on this phone. 'By."

Jack Kincaid hung up the phone with a slam and beckoned to Thorne. "Here we go, Sergeant. Let's shake a leg."

He hurried out the door almost at a trot.

The little coupe left the main gate and whined up into a shrieking roar. Kincaid held his foot hard on the accelerator, pushing it to the floor and shouting delightedly at Thorne above the sound of the supercharged motor.

"Watch this bundle of bolts hit ninety. Hopped her up myself."

Thorne could smell burned rubber as Kincaid pulled on the emergency in front of a no-parking sign at Pennsylvania Avenue and Ninth Street in downtown Washington. Kincaid was out of the car almost before it stopped rolling.

"Wait here, Thorne. Be out in a minute."

With that he rushed into the FBI Headquarters, unfastening his wallet as he hurried to get his pass out for the guard at the front door.

Fifteen minutes later he was back, and they were off again at a wild clip through the downtown traffic. Thorne heard the screams of sirens behind them. He turned to see two motorcycle policemen bearing down.

"Looks like you're in for it, Jack. Here comes the law."

Thorne was amazed at his own easy familiarity

with the Texan, but events of the day had brought a closer understanding between them. The sergeant now believed that their first feeling of warmth was cementing into friendship.

Silver Chief hung his head out of the window, ears flattened back in the rushing wind. He was obviously enjoying the ride, and was prepared to take his cue from his master. Since he felt no tension from the men within the car, Chief was satisfied merely to gaze haughtily at the policeman who drew alongside, frantically waving for them to pull over. Obviously the officer recognized Kincaid, for after a glance he grinned and waved them on. Thorne could no longer contain his curiosity.

"Jack, where are we headed?" he asked. "What's all the rush?"

Kincaid did not take his eyes from the road as he answered.

"Good thing you've got your bag in the back seat."

"Why?"

"The Inter-Continental Bomber Command is holding a B-50 for us at Andrews Air Force Base. Just caught them in time. They had their props turning over when we phoned . . ."

"A bomber! But where are we headed?"

Kincaid turned left, skirting the broad Potomac River, partly frozen over and its shore line whitened with frost.

"We're going to San Francisco, Pete. So you see we've called it right."

"How is that?"

"Our man tried to sneak out of the side gate of the Embassy," Jack explained. "He was driven to

National Airport and took off on a commercial airliner for Frisco."

"Those commercial planes make a thirty-minute
stop in Kansas City. Ours will be a nonstop flight
and we'll be in San Francisco before he arrives. FBI
agents will be on hand at Kansas City, but will not
try to detain the man, the idea being to find out
whom he will contact on the coast. They will be part
of the reception committee. I hope we'll have no
slip-ups."

"Both of us," Thorne added.

"Incidentally," Kincaid went on, "I have some information about that piece of cloth that was analyzed.
But it will keep. What we need now is speed."

Chapter 10

CROSS-COUNTRY

WITH his usual abandon, Kincaid drove his car directly out onto the apron in front of the operation shack, and was followed by incredulous stares as he ignored every rule in the book. Before he could open his door, it was pulled wide by a frantic-looking young man carrying a bulging brief case.

"Here you are, Mr. Kincaid. We've put all needed information in here. The San Francisco office has been alerted and will pick you up. We could find only one pair of slacks and two shirts in your locker at the office. I guess that will have to do."

Kincaid shouted over the roar of the idling engines nearby.

"Thanks, Morgan, sign me out at the office. Who's the skipper of yon crate?" While he was talking, Sergeant Thorne hurried around to the trunk compartment and yanked out his Army-type canvas bag. Silver Chief stood nearby quietly awaiting orders, meantime watching Thorne closely and feeling and responding to the urgency and excitement all about.

"Colonel Winrod, Mr. Kincaid," answered Morgan. "Come on over and I'll help you aboard. They've been idling here for fifteen minutes."

"Tough," was Kincaid's laconic reply as he headed toward the huge silver Air Force plane.

Thorne realized he was about to enter the most gigantic plane he had ever laid eyes on. It towered above them grim and businesslike and as high as a four-story building. Silver Chief walked obediently at heel beside his master.

The group came up under the nose of the great ship, between four slowly revolving propellers. Thorne saw an open hatch with a small aluminum ladder dangling from the dark mouth of the underside of the ship. It seemed as though they were all about to be swallowed up into the underslung jaw of a mammoth silver shark.

An arm came down through the opening and grasped Kincaid's brief case, then Thorne's bag. The former was whisked aboard by the same strong, steady assistant, who looked once at Silver Chief, then at Thorne. Wordlessly Thorne bent down and picked up Silver Chief. Helped by Morgan from below and the khaki-covered arm from above, he climbed the swaying ladder. With a lunge Silver Chief scrambled aboard, followed by Sergeant Thorne.

No sooner had his feet cleared the deck than the ladder was withdrawn and the hatch slammed shut and bolted. Thorne could feel the slight movement as the plane gained momentum.

Although he was still on his knees, Thorne looked about. He realized he was in the lower part of the forward cockpit. Directly ahead he could see the bombardier's plexiglass compartment—aptly named the Greenhouse. Above that, and slightly forward, sat the flight captain and his copilot. To the rear was the navigator's office, and on the other side sat the flight engineer.

The whole forward end of the ship was covered from floor to ceiling with a maze of instruments and gauges such as Thorne had visualized only in nightmares—dials, gauges, levers, pulleys, radio, radar—every conceivable device for the flying safety of the crew, all too busy now at their appointed tasks to pay any attention to their newly arrived guests.

Kincaid also gazed about in awe and admiration. That part of the cockpit was covered with cool green matting that acted as an insulation against the noise of the propellers and also against the cold, although the entire ship was pressurized for long-range, high-altitude flights. The floor covering gave the whole area a restful, cozy atmosphere.

As they were softly airborne, Kincaid said to Thorne, "This is one of the new babies. She's a beaut, all right."

Thorne merely nodded in agreement. Silver Chief half crouched, half huddled against his master, unafraid apparently, but hoping for a friendly, reassuring pat.

As soon as they were safely aloft and straightened away on course, all the while climbing for altitude, the pilot, a lean, good-looking lieutenant colonel, slipped out of his seat, turned the controls over to his copilot, and walked back to greet his passengers.

"Welcome aboard the good ship *Lana T*, gentlemen. We're not used to carrying passengers, but we offer you the hospitality of the ship. You'll be more comfortable aft, if you don't mind climbing down the subway through the bomb bay. It's a little cramped getting through, but I'm sure you'll be better off back there. If there is anything you need or want, our crew chief will get it for you. Chow's served in about two and a half hours.

"We're going up over the weather to forty thousand feet, so you may not be able to see Chicago tonight, but it will be on our starboard if you want to try to catch it out of the belly gun blister.

"Our estimated time of arrival will be around midnight, California time. I believe we will overtake the commercial plane somewhere west of Denver, though we will be far above them. I understand we will land at Mills Field, the Municipal Airport, at San Francisco, where you will be met. Let me show you the easiest way down the subway."

The colonel led them to the fire wall forming the back of the padded forward compartment. He unlatched a small square door that led down a narrow tunnel, black, dark and cold. This was the bomb bay, where the "eggs" of destruction were stored before they were dropped. There was no pressurized air in this compartment, and already it was deadly cold. Kincaid went first, crawling on all fours into the blackness. Thorne next shoved Silver Chief in, who crept resolutely ahead, occasionally looking back to see that Peter Thorne was following.

Soon they were helped out into the spacious belly of the ship. Here again all was efficiency, here the comfort of the crew was of primary interest. The entire interior was packed with equipment of one sort or another carefully stowed along the walls and labeled in stencils for easy reading. Thorne noticed ammunition for the two waist guns, more for the bottom turret, and even farther aft for the tail gunner; also primus stoves, flares, life rafts, life preservers, food in tins, first-aid kits, even folding cots for long flights. In flight the *Lana T* took on the aspect of a sumptuous flying home for her crew, which was exactly the way she had been planned. Seated on a cot surrounded by a sheaf of papers he had taken from his brief case, Kincaid beckoned the sergeant over to his side. First, however, Thorne wanted to be sure that his dog was taken care of, but he had no need to worry on that score. Chief had immediately become a pet of the crew, who hailed him as a welcome diversion on the flight. Accustomed to kindness and the curiosity of people, the dog trotted amiably from one to another, making friends. Thorne could not help smiling at the complacent way Chief accepted the attentions of his admirers.

Kincaid indicated a place at his side and told Thorne to sit down.

"We might as well get some of this paper work digested now," he explained. "This flight may be our last chance to catch up." As he gazed down on the bulk of detailed typing, he asked with a grimace, "You have all this paper work in your outfit?"

Thorne's smile was rueful, as he remembered the endless reports he was asked to fill out, to read and to study. Yes, he well knew the drudgery of such labor and considered it the unglamorous part of crime detection. He realized, though, that such study was more often than not the basis for spectacular arrests, which the press often labeled "lucky breaks."

"Yes, we go through about the same procedure," he told Jack, who was thumbing through the pages again.

Kincaid looked up suddenly. "This first batch is concerned with what we obtained from your description. There are possibly seven men in the United States and Canada who closely fit the bill of your first suspect. Five of these have Russian connections and are under surveillance at this moment. As to the shorter man—as we call him—we have data on seventy-six. Since his description was more vague, we had to include more in the grouping and also came up with less accurate and less detailed information. Fourteen of these suspects have connections with Russia, either through family, birth or business. They have all had criminal records or have tangled with our governments, so it was simple to get their descriptions. Of course, the men we're after might never have brushed up against the law, a fact that I, for one, am inclined to believe. For a plot of this scope, new blood is often used."

Thorne, however, did not agree. "You are unquestionably right, Jack, in your methods of procedure. But I believe the way those men knew their way around the North Country, and the expert timing involved in their plan, precludes the possibility that they had never come in contact with the law. In the dead of winter that wasteland is no place for amateurs."

"Agreed. But they could have been recent imports into the country," Kincaid said. "If, however, we do accept the fact that these agents must be known to us, it will narrow down our present findings even more."

"You've done a remarkable job of narrowing down already," the sergeant added sincerely. "But somehow I keep feeling that we should get back to where the whole thing started. That seemed to be the center of all activity."

"The center of *all* activity, Peter? How about the hotel in Washington?"

Thorne smiled at the joke at his expense. "I see what you mean. But I still believe that my country holds more clues than those we've uncovered up to now."

"Perhaps."

Kincaid continued to read through the papers. "Oh, yes," he continued, "here is the analysis of that bit of cloth. To me it is extremely important and offers practical possibilities for action."

"In what way?" Thorne asked.

"Well —to start from scratch, here's how it goes. The cloth is made of domestic wool and was manufactured for one of the biggest wholesale suit and coat chains in the country. It comes from a mill in North Carolina. Because of the vast quantity of suits sold by this chain, they make up the yarns in slightly different weaves for specific sections in the country. This is done at the source to spot-check for volume and production control, to determine customer preference. This weave was sold on the West Coast. So, my friend, don't be in too much of a hurry to get back to the wilds of Canada."

"Touché!" The sergeant smiled. "And what else have you discovered to establish my proper place?"

"Well . . . There are microscopic traces of tobacco and bits of ends of paper matches. The matches were easily traced, being made by a San Francisco company and given away in packs with every purchase of cigarettes. The tobacco is either English or Canadian. There's a note here stating that if the staff had more time, they could have established the exact brand. The present guess is Gold-Flake. Presuming this to be correct, a check was made of all stores in San Francisco selling cigarettes. Out of the thirty-one hundred retail outlets, only twenty-three stock Gold-Flakes. Needless to say, all these places will be watched—just in case.

"Of course, your would-be murderer is not there, nor is there any chance of his arriving before we do. But we often find that foreign agents have very similar habits—particularly in such small indulgences as smoking. So at least we may be able to get a line on some of his buddies, who are unquestionably waiting out there."

"I see. In other words, any of the men on your suspect list found in or about San Francisco, or purchasing those cigarettes, will at once come under observation."

"Exactly," Kincaid replied. "But in a way, the most helpful sign from the point of view of our problem lies in their anxiety to get you out of the way. This shows clearly that they have not managed to get the crate out of the country, or they would not care any more. It's your possible identification that might gum up their deal."

"I hope to have a chance to gum it up, believe you me," the sergeant vowed.

The crew chief came up at that moment, bringing aluminum trays containing plates of hot stew. Supplemented by sliced peaches and black coffee, the sergeant and Kincaid enjoyed a thoroughly pleasant meal, miles above central United States. As they were drinking their second cup of coffee, one of the waist gunners glanced casually at his watch, immediately poked his head out of a curved blister on one side of the plane and spoke to his opposite partner, in charge of the radar-aimed gun.

"Ought to be headin' right over Homeplate in a couple of minutes, I reckon. Wonder where the Brass is going to send us next? Rio or Guam?"

"What difference?" was the answer. "This training stuff is just like riding trolley cars when I was a kid. Who cares where we get off, just so long as we get home okay?"

Thorne could make little sense out of this talk, so he turned to Kincaid for some kind of translation.

"It's like this," Jack explained. "The ship we're on is part of the Strategic Air Command. 'Homeplate' is a baseball term as you probably know. I imagine it's the slang for their Command Headquarters, which is somewhere below us near Omaha, Nebraska. Offut Air Force Base, I think it's called.

"As you can see from this ship, all flights are made under combat conditions, and no fooling around. For all I know we may be flying with a full bomb load. There may be even live bombs out there in the bomb bay we crawled through."

"They certainly look live enough," Thorne commented. "By the way, Jack, just how does the Strategic Air Command function?"

"In more ways than I know, but I can tell you about some of them. This arm of the service is pre-

pared to strike within minutes of being ordered into
the air. The men fly all over the world on these
training flights—testing bomb loads, crew fatigue,
navigational problems and innumerable other factors
that might arise, if and when the 'wild-blue-yonder'
boys might have to pay off with the real stuff.

"Incidentally, their Headquarters was notified
about the small monoplane you described for us.
Any strange craft picked up leaving the North American Continent will be contacted and, if suspicious,
it will be requested to land. Refusing, it will be shot
down. This is one safety umbrella we taxpayers have
over our heads night and day, three hundred and
sixty-five days in the year."

Thorne was silent for a moment, musing on the
possibilities that, if the Russians should get hold of
the stolen crate, this air umbrella might not give
much security. He mentioned this to Jack.

"If you don't think our governments realize this,"
Kincaid said, "let me give you a little more data.
The Radar Control Net circling our countries is on
the alert, as well as every Jet Interceptor Wing from
Alaska to Panama, Greenland to South America. If
you are *still* not convinced, let me add that the Navy
has also made available subs and subchasers in the
air group, just in case the Russians try to sneak a
submarine into some harbor!"

As Kincaid elaborated on the Government's effort
to prevent the dikortrium from falling into Russian
hands, Thorne remembered his serious talk with the
Minister of Defense in Ottawa. Somehow, in spite of
accumulating evidence that San Francisco was the
present focal point of search, his thoughts kept re-

turning to the wild frontier country that he knew best.

"Well, that's about it," Kincaid finished. He carefully replaced all the papers in his brief case and moved across the belly of the plane to a bunk that had been prepared for him.

"We have about four more hours to San Francisco, Pete. I'm going to try to get some sleep if you don't mind."

As the sergeant started to reply, Kincaid put his head down, using his arms for a pillow, and closed his eyes. A few minutes later Thorne followed suit, the faraway drone of the engines lulling him to sleep too. As if this was the proper procedure at the time, Silver Chief stretched himself on the floor as close as he could to his master, his even breathing soon showing that he too was asleep.

Hours later, awakened by one of the crewmen, the sergeant and Kincaid simultaneously looked at their watches. It was 3:12 A.M. Eastern Standard Time. Allowing the three hours for Pacific Time, they were about to land, only three minutes later than Colonel Winrod's ETA (Estimated Time of Arrival).

The huge B-50 made a perfect landing and taxied quickly up the apron near a dark hangar. As soon as the monkey ladder was lowered, a man in civilian clothes stepped from the shadows, and inquired for Thorne and Kincaid. After the stranger had introduced himself, using identification previously agreed upon, the three men drew deeper into the shadows for a talk.

The California agent briefed Kincaid and Thorne quickly. The commercial airliner would arrive in approximately fifty minutes, having been delayed by head winds. Authorities in Kansas City had definitely established the fact that the wanted man was on the plane, but they had been given orders not to stop him there.

Thorne expressed the hope that no arrest would be made at the airport in San Francisco either. "For he may lead us to more important members of his gang," the sergeant added.

Kincaid agreed, with reservations. "We have a way to establish whether this man really *is* a member of the gang we're after," he explained. "While you are making your identification, I'll use the glass the professor gave us. That will determine if he has come in contact with the ore. If so, we will follow him; if not, it would be my idea to pick him up here and now and see if we can't get some quick information. Don't forget, Pete, three and a half days have passed since the crate was stolen."

An hour later the loud-speaker system at the airport announced, "Flight 24, from New York, Washington, and Kansas City, arriving at San Francisco Airport."

Thorne, Kincaid and Silver Chief stepped into the shadow of a parked gasoline truck and watched the landing ramp being wheeled up to the airliner. Thorne nudged Kincaid. "I'll bump into the man I think is the one," he whispered. "You put the glass on him and then give Silver Chief a command."

Kincaid asked also in a whisper, "What do you mean?"

Thorne patted his dog's head and then looked at Jack.

"Silver Chief will make the positive identification."

Jack looked down at the dog. "What do I say to the dog?"

Thorne answered him with one brief word: "Go!"

The passengers disembarked slowly down the ramp and made for the exit gate. Thorne spotted in the middle of the crowd a man carrying a leather brief case. He walked toward him and with what seemed to be an accidental motion, bumped into his shoulder. The other U.S. agent closed in from the other side of the plane. Meanwhile Kincaid was carefully observing the man through the dark, blue-green piece of glass. Without looking down, he gave a sharp but low-voiced order: "Silver Chief! Go!"

With a lunge, the dog sprang from the shadows of the truck and ran among the passengers getting off the plane. His ears were laid back, his teeth bared. The man with the brief case took one look at the snarling dog and turned to run, but he did not get more than a few steps before Thorne and the California agent had him by the elbows.

"You are under arrest for attempted murder and conspiracy against the United States Government," the West Coast agent said. "Come this way quietly."

The stranger gave a helpless little shrug, and without further talk he was disarmed and led to a waiting limousine. Thorne and his dog sat in front with the driver, the others in the rear of the car on either side of the prisoner. As they sped along toward the center of the city, Kincaid fired question after question at his captive, only to be met with stony silence.

Exasperated, Kincaid said, "Look, friend, we've

already got you on two Federal counts. Then there
is that little matter of attempted murder. The man
up front can prove the attack. You may not remember it, but he was your victim. But look now—if you
come clean about your other activities, we might play
down the assault charge when we get to Headquarters."

"And if I don't . . ."

"You'll get the maximum, that's what!" Kincaid
snapped. "You could make it a lot easier for yourself
by leading us to your buddies."

"I have no buddies."

After this denial the prisoner sat in tense, thin-
lipped silence, seeming far away and deep within his
own thoughts. Suddenly he started to cough, softly at
first, but the paroxysms grew so violent that he
seemed about to choke. He reached in a pocket for a
handkerchief which he held in front of his lips. Soon
the spasms grew less violent, and when he could speak
again, he turned to Kincaid.

"I have more to fear than what you can do to me.
I will not speak. Not now. Not *ever!*"

As Kincaid stared at him, the prisoner's defiance
and intention became crystal-clear. That subtle maneuver with a handkerchief had no relation whatever
to his cough!

"Stop the car!" Jack demanded. "Let's see if we
can get help for this man."

"No help . . . too late," the prisoner muttered
through ashen lips.

The car pulled to a stop on the side of the highway.
As Kincaid tried to haul his prisoner out, he slumped

to the floor, his breath leaving him in the rattle of a dying man.

The others had now gathered to the side of the car.

"How did you know he was sick?" the sergeant asked, as they straightened the body out on the floor.

Unanswering, Kincaid gazed down into staring, unseeing eyes and felt for a pulse that did not beat.

"The man is dead," Jack announced wearily. "Poisoned himself with a vial concealed in his handkerchief."

Wordlessly they gazed at one another for a moment, then Jack directed that they should be driven to the morgue. On their way again, he mused out loud, as if in need to reassure himself:

"Of course we can get his fingerprints and send them to every country in the world. But it may take days to get information and trace the man's identity. Something has *got* to break in this case pretty soon! But examine the pattern, Pete. Always the same. The man Daroff would rather hang in Canada than talk. And now this one kills himself rather than give his name or information. He told the truth too. He had more to fear than what we can do to him. With us, at least, he would have had a chance to be heard. With his buddies, no. And evidently being captured is as great a crime as any. They'd have bumped him off without a qualm. They'd stop at nothing."

The memory of a vicious face and of being left in the snow to die swam into Thorne's mind.

"You're right, Jack," he said. "They would stop at nothing. And I ought to know!"

Chapter 11

SILVER CHIEF MAKES A DISCOVERY

AFTER leaving the body at the morgue the California agent directed the driver to proceed along the Embarcadero and then to turn up into the hills behind the Presidio.

"We are quartering you in an apartment belonging to one of our agents. The place is on Pacific Heights," he explained. "It's an ideal hide-out because of the many streets and highways nearby. The apartment is on the ground floor, with entrances to two streets and another out on to the alley. You can get in and out of the place without being followed too easily."

Once inside, Thorne and Kincaid had to agree that the location was practical for their purpose. It was also an attractively furnished place with a beautiful view overlooking the Presidio and Golden Gate Bridge. There were not too many apartments or houses in the immediate vicinity, yet it was not so isolated as to attract attention. Another advantage was the accessibility to Golden Gate Park, where Silver Chief could run and be exercised.

After their nap on the plane, neither Thorne nor Kincaid felt a need for further rest. Instead, they decided to have some coffee and continue a final study of the reports. Both men believed that the following days would be spent in actively tracking down the enemy. Thorne was excited at the prospect of starting out. His work in the wilds of Canada had conditioned him to go in pursuit; his was the tradition of first-hand personal contacts, stalking the foe over vast dreary spaces, and he was resolved to take in the men whom he had been assigned to deliver, dead or alive!

Meanwhile, after the California agent had gone, Thorne was willing again to go over the facts and findings contained in the reports. Silver Chief seemed to feel otherwise about the inactivity. It seemed as though the dog realized that the time was near when he and his master would become a team once more, depending on each other in stalking their foe. Chief paced up and down, sniffing the confining quarters as if they could not possibly contain the answer to his eager, restless energy.

Occasionally Kincaid looked up from his work to see if Thorne was noticing his dog's behavior. At one point, when Chief looked as if he might burst into speech, Kincaid broke into a hearty laugh.

"Take a look at that dog of yours, Pete," he said. "Hanged if he doesn't seem to know what our plans are. Do you two really talk together?"

Thorne smiled. "Of course we do. And I don't mean only when I am saying words either. Silver Chief can read my mind, can't you, fellow?"

Unlike his usual habit when spoken to in warm, affectionate tones, Chief did not go up to his master to be fondled. Instead, he planted himself in front of Thorne, his head cocked in a definite attitude of questioning.

Both men laughed, but Chief did not budge till his master spoke again. "Tomorrow, Chief, we'll take off tomorrow. Go in the other room and lie down until we're finished here. Lie down."

Chief trotted away obediently.

The first faint fingers of dawn poked over the eastern hills beyond Sausalito across the bay before the sergeant again looked up from his work. Kincaid was still making notes in a small leather book which he carried for quick references when out in the field. When Thorne rose and stood there stretching, Kincaid put down his pencil with a weary sigh.

"What say we knock off, Pete?" he suggested. "It's five-fifteen in the morning. If you've never seen a dawn come up over San Francisco Harbor, my advice would be to go out and get yourself some air and see it. It's one of the most beautiful sights in the world— sometimes even more dramatic than the famous sunsets around here.

"As a matter of fact, you can take Chief out for a walk. I'm sure he could stand a good run. There aren't any people around the park at this hour. You can slip off his harness and let him romp. I think I'll have a smoke and turn in for a couple of hours. Nothing much we can do till the city wakes up."

"Good idea, Jack," replied Thorne. "I was just wondering about a little walk. That plane ride sort of stiffened my leg. I'd like to work it out a bit, then I'll come back for a nap myself. From the way you talk, we're going to be doing a lot of walking."

"Yes, looks that way. I'll wake you up around eight-thirty."

Thorne slipped the leather leash on Silver Chief

and let him out the back door, down the alley to the street, where they both looked carefully around, but could not see anyone stirring.

Shortly they came to the park, which was inviting and cool in the early-morning sunshine. Heavy dew still clung to the evergreens and the sparse winter grass. The air was brisk and clear. For the first time since arriving in the United States, Thorne felt a lift in his spirits and a bounce to his walk. He could understand the lure and attraction of this great city—especially on such a morning. He unsnapped Silver Chief's leash and, with a happy bark, the dog was off, coursing through thickets, sniffing the air and rolling puppylike on the carefully tended grass.

Meanwhile, Thorne walked along a gravel path. Released from detail work and exhilarated from the walk, his mind had free play. Thoughts went back to the time, four days before, when that call of help had come from Pilot Landry—a brave man whose lips were sealed forever! Again the sergeant renewed his firm resolve to avenge the brutal murder and settle all the other scores as well! With Silver Chief to help he would not fail!

Presently Thorne could hear the swish of tires on the asphalt. Though he could not see beyond a mass of high-banked foliage, the sergeant realized that he was moving parallel to a highway winding through Golden Gate Park.

He looked around to get bearings of the direction he had taken and be certain of a direct course to the apartment should he wish to hurry back. As he did so, Thorne noticed that Silver Chief was standing stock-still, peering between the branches of a large

rhododendron bush as he busily tested the air. When
Chief's ruff rose in unexplained anger, the sergeant
froze in his tracks. He gave the dog a low-voiced command; it was too late. With a low, ominous growl
Silver Chief raced toward the road, crashing through
shrubs and bushes. Thorne had no course of action
except to run along the path, calling to his dog and
trying to keep him in sight.

Meanwhile, Silver Chief was enjoying himself for
the first time since he had left Canada. With leg
healed, his spirits rising from his frolic in the park,
he was thoroughly in the mood for action. The smell
of earth and the space to stretch his legs brought
associations of the dreary trek through forests when
his quarry had escaped. Seldom coming off second-
best with criminals, Chief was frustrated with desire
to amend this failure.

When he first entered the park he trotted around
sampling the delightful odor of dew-damp grass and
fragrant breezes, feeling only a vague sense of that
which he sought. Presently though, past and present
merged in sharp awareness. Furiously he began casting around to come directly upon the menacing
scent. Then at last he was on the track that must be
followed. It was clearly and unmistakably that of the
enemy. It was then that Thorne gave a soft-spoken
order, but even a wildly shouted command would
not have halted Chief's drive toward the body scent
in his nostrils. He bolted straight and true as an arrow
toward the source.

Thorne was already running toward his dog. He
could hear Chief hurtling through the underbrush

without pause or caution. Only one motive drove Silver Chief onward: revenge!

The dog burst through snapping twigs and onto a clear, lawn-covered slope bordering the road. Directly ahead, Chief saw his quarry—the huge and hated Chelkar, the strange dog that had stood over his own master's prostrate body in the faraway Canadian North woods!

This beast was being led toward a limousine which stood with its motor running. When he was about fifteen feet from the car, Chelkar sensed some nameless peril from behind and glanced backward.

With a ferocious snarl he turned to meet his attacker, almost throwing the guard off his feet. Whatever might be said of Chelkar's faults, cowardice was not one of them. His lips curled over wicked, discolored teeth, and his short ears flattened back against his enormous skull as he braced himself to meet Silver Chief's attack. The man holding the leash gave a frantic tug as he half dragged Chelkar toward the waiting car.

Silver Chief shot forward without slackening his pace, his teeth bared. With his eighty pounds flung forward, he slashed at his huge opponent. That bloody taste of flesh was a joy, as he sank into the flank of his hated opponent!

The impact of Chief's body knocked Chelkar off balance, thus enabling the terrified guard to drag his burden to within a few feet of the car. Chief rolled over twice on the dew-slippery grass before he regained his own balance. By that time a driver had stepped from the car and opened the door.

Chelkar tried to rise and escape the torment of being dragged along. The guard, observing blood streaming from the dog's ripped shoulder, lifted the snarling beast and threw him on the back seat of the car, jumped in and slammed the door—all this in one hasty, terrified motion. Before Silver Chief could charge again, the car had moved away, gears whining as they shifted into high.

Thorne had now burst through the thickets and into the clear of the slope just in time to see the final act of a swiftly played drama. He saw Chief futilely trying to catch up with the limousine, from which the face of a savage beast peered through the rear window. He tried to read the license plate, but reflected light blotted out the numerals. There was only one other thing to try, but even as the sergeant drew out his revolver, he realized that the vehicle had pulled far out of range.

He then shouted at Silver Chief, who turned reluctantly to join his master. Thorne ran his practiced hands over Chief's legs and body to see if he had sustained any injury in his encounter with the wolfhound. Though Chief himself was unhurt, Thorne noticed that pieces of flesh and blood were smeared over the dog's whiskers and jaws. A slow grin spread on the sergeant's face.

"Good work, Chief," he said. "So the monster has returned. He could not have come alone! You found them, didn't you, fellow? Come on. Let's be getting back. Kincaid will certainly want to know about this!"

He hastily slipped the leash on Silver Chief and they headed back to the apartment.

Chapter 12

THE ENEMY

IN A secluded run-down house, not far from where the furious dog fight occurred, three men sat around a rough kitchen table sipping coffee from thick white mugs. All were dressed in soiled T-shirts, their trousers variations of the heavy, blue work-type garment. These men spoke earnestly and rapidly in Russian, one of them dominating the conversation.

Unwashed dishes were stacked in the sink of this ill-kept rendezvous, and the old-fashioned black stove was cluttered with grease-filled pans. A single vegetable dish placed in the center of the table served as a community ash tray.

Two doors led from the kitchen, one opening into a room that had been a bedroom, but was now an ultramodern radio broadcasting and receiving headquarters. Both walls and ceiling were soundproofed, and the radio equipment was of the best quality procurable. In front of the dials and knobs a young man sat listening intently through earphones; short-wave and microwave broadcasts of the police, the aircraft and the ships at sea could be heard from the various speakers. Everything of importance that could be picked up was tuned in and monitored for information.

In the kitchen a large man badly in need of a shave was speaking in loud tones of authority.

"I must tell you again," he declaimed, "it is of the utmost importance that we remove from this country the prize we have worked so hard to secure. We have planned well, and there must be no failure, even if we must give our lives in the attempt. I have received strict orders from MVD that our mission is one that might well mean world domination. We have other means of knowing that this is true. The Americans have gone to all lengths to intercept and decode mes-

sages. Their frenzied activity indicates that this secret ore is of world-wide significance. It must reach Russia and be placed in the hands of our distinguished scientists. Then we will know."

One of the men snuffed out his cigarette with a gesture of exasperation before he spoke.

"But, Illych, why do we not try the original plan— allowing a neutral vessel to be intercepted by one of our submarines, which will remove this seemingly insignificant box."

"Fool; do not speak of such lunacy," growled

Illych. "Can you not hear the radio? The U.S. and
the Canadian Governments have both alerted their
navies. Submarines—both detector and killer types—
are armed and on the alert, as are their search planes.
The submarine attempt has been abandoned for the
moment.

"It was our intention to try to send a small piece
of this ore by diplomatic pouch, but our Consulate
in San Francisco has warned that all mail and packages leaving here and Canada are being screened and
tested. Even those addressed to neutral countries are
examined.

"Under no conditions," the man continued, "must
we risk exposing our plan to remove this substance
to Russia. We must wait until a crack appears in the
vigilance of the enemy. I know these so-called demo-
cratic people. Always they relax; then our time will
come."

"But what method will we use?" a young man
named Boris asked.

"There are two alternatives, both highly dangerous."

The leader paused to glare at his underlings for
not contributing some solution to their problem.
Unconsciously he kept biting his lip so that pain
mingled with anger on his face. Illych let out a bel-
low, revealing an ugly gap where his two front teeth
should have been. Not one person at the table smiled,
knowing that the matter of those missing teeth was
a sore subject. To cover his confusion, the man
roared:

"Stelka . . . Get Stelka awake. There is much to
be done. We will not wait for official orders from

Moscow. I will take the responsibility. Every day we linger in this accursed country it becomes more dangerous and difficult to function."

There was a slight pause before one of the men interrupted meekly:

"Stelka has not yet returned from his morning walk with Chelkar. He should be back soon."

Illych ground a fist angrily into the palm of his other hand. "Why does that fool insist on taking my dog all the way across the bridge to Golden Gate Park?" he stormed. "There must be plenty of nearby places where the beast could exercise. Stelka is a fool. He wastes much time!"

"Yes, Comrade Illych," young Boris agreed.

At that moment Stelka arrived, his moonface creased with lines of worry, followed by Chelkar and the driver. After relocking the rear door through which they had entered, they rushed into the room where Illych and the others waited.

Noting the expression on Stelka's face and the beaten look of the battered Chelkar, Illych leaped to his feet.

"What is it, Comrade?" he cried. "What has happened?"

The sound of their leader's voice rising to such a pitch caused tense curiosity among the men; even the radio operator appeared in the doorway to see what had happened.

Before answering, Stelka took Chelkar to the kitchen sink and, while washing the dog's wounds with a soiled cloth, he spoke reflectively:

"It was the huge white dog from the North, Illych —the one we have heard so much about. The animal

attacked Chelkar in Golden Gate Park. He seemed
to be alone. Though perhaps his master was also in
the vicinity."

"That is not only possible, but probable," Illych
growled. "If the Canadian has tracked us here, that
may explain why Feodor did not arrive from Washington."

"Feodor from Washington!" Stelka exclaimed.

"That's right! Feodor, our best man to handle such
a situation, seems to have failed. You know what that
means."

As Illych addressed this to his men, the room became eloquent with silence.

"It seems that you do know," Illych added coldly.
"We cannot permit failures. It is dangerous to have
around us those who fail. There are ways . . ."

"We know, Comrade," Stelka said appeasingly.

"Are you positive the dog who fought with Chelkar
is directly connected with our search?" Illych asked.
"If so, Feodor was evidently followed here from
Washington. We must not underestimate the
enemy."

"This dog was no stray," Stelka returned.

"Both Mario and I saw him. He fitted the description we were given. . . . Almost as large and powerful
as Chelkar, his coat white as the snow on the steppes
of Russia, and he fights with the cunning and ferocity
of a tiger. There is no doubt—it was the dog called
Silver Chief. He seemed to know that Chelkar was
his mortal enemy . . ."

Again Illych sputtered. "The Canadian has been
carefully watched and followed from the time he left
Ottawa, Canada, to give Feodor a perfect opportunity

to kill him. It is inconceivable that this blundering policeman escaped our agent."

Stelka was patient, but equally as firm in his opinion.

"Inconceivable or not, Comrade Illych, it is time we do something. For where that dog is, there also is his master. The mounted policeman is not far behind. You know their reputation. Only death will keep them from the trail . . ."

Illych stared at Stelka for a long instant, a shrewd, cunning look creeping into his piglike eyes. "Yes, Stelka, you are right. This is not the time for wishful thinking. We must act, and act fast. I have already told our Comrades here that I will assume the responsibility for our alternate plan. Our primary idea is to get that box into the hands of Soviet scientists. I know now what we must do.

"Boris, go into the radio room and relieve Lackvief. Tell him to go upstairs at once and help Comrade Richiensky pack what we will need for Plans B and C. We must hurry now.

"Also send to Washington one brief question about Feodor in our ultrahigh-frequency code. Make it short. Feodor is supposed to be here. The Americans no doubt will have their transmitter detectors in this area working twenty-four hours, now that we have been traced to this locality."

Illych glanced across the room at the men, all of whom were intent upon his words in this sudden crisis. "All of you know what to do, where to go and whom to see. We will begin to pack and clear out at once. We will abandon Chelkar here and now." Illych threw Stelka a long, meaningful look. "The

dog has been nothing but a burden and a trial to us
from the beginning. His usefulness is ended."

Stelka returned the look with one of equal meaning and understanding. He glanced down at the dog,
then back to Illych.

"Comrade Illych," he said, "I think you are making a mistake. Chelkar has given us faithful service.
He will be useful where we are going. Also, if he is
found dead or alive it will only confirm our presence
in these parts. As I told you, I am not certain that
the dog who fought with Chelkar is the same as the
one from the North Country. Nor am I now really
certain that he was followed, and if he was, whether
we were seen—much less identified. Also, this strange
dog *might* have been a stray."

Illych smiled mockingly. "A highly trained dog
such as the one you describe attacking Chelkar for
no reason? Highly improbable, Stelka. You made
your point too well *the first time!* But anyhow, for
the present, let us assume that Chelkar may prove
of future value. He goes with us. Commence notify-
ing our agents—and the Embassy, of course. It might
take hours to have a reply from them. Save enough
food for lunch and pack sandwiches. Tonight we put
Plan B into effect."

Efficiently and like ponderous automatons, the
men fell to their tasks. Soon the rooms upstairs and
down were echoing to sounds of crates being nailed
together, heavy boxes being pushed across the floors
and suitcases placed near the kitchen door. By noon
most of the packing had been completed and everything attended to except the final dismantling of
radio and telegraph equipment. While the men sat

around smoking and waiting further orders, Boris brought in a sheet of yellow paper and handed it to the leader.

Illych frowned as he read the message, but instead of disclosing the contents, he stuffed the sheet into his pocket. From the radio room, where the equipment was being carefully dismantled, came muttering complaints. Illych shouted for the operator to come and tell him what the trouble was.

"Comrade Illych," the man said, "it seems to me that the heavy sea air has gotten into our carefully packed cases and has corroded most of the batteries we use in our portable sets. It would be too bad to let this equipment go because of lack of batteries. I think . . ."

"Never mind what you think, Comrade. Keep quiet and get back to work. It is obvious that we need new batteries. I will get them myself. Where is my driver? Mario! Mario!"

But the young man who had driven Stelka and the dog in the park was already buttoning his coat.

"Right here and ready, Comrade," he answered.

"Good. We will go into the city to a hardware store and get batteries. If anything more is needed, write what you want on a list. But hurry, all of you. I have just received word that from now on we are on our own. We have to function mostly without orders. Communications in all cities are being carefully watched.

"Evidently there is great determination among U.S. authorities that we shall not leave the country with our box. Even the Radar Defense Net has been put on a twenty-four-hour alert. So—we will change our

plans slightly and go a little south of our originally
decided point. This will take us inside the perimeter
of the Radar Net. But we must have those batteries."

Illych turned to Boris.

"Can our sets reach out an additional three hundred miles, Comrade?"

"Most likely, if atmospheric conditions are at all
favorable and the batteries fresh. Be sure to look at
the dates of all you buy. Accept no old ones. Storage
weakens their strength."

"I will see that they are fresh," Illych replied. "Is
the list ready? Let us go."

One of the men thrust a paper into the leader's
hand as he strode toward the door held open by
Mario. Illych turned on the threshold.

"Stelka, I charge you to see that no one leaves this
house. It is risk enough for me to travel about in
broad daylight. But I am your leader and must take
risks for the Cause. Meanwhile, Stelka, you may be
the leader in this house . . ." Here Illych showed his
gums in an ugly grin . . . "and, my dear Comrade,
a leader never leaves his post!"

"I shall not leave," Stelka replied steadily.

When they reached downtown San Francisco, the
driver was careful not to break traffic rules or attract
attention. The two stolid-looking men in inconspicuous wearing apparel would not have caused the
slightest notice. The technique of blending into any
gathering was an important phase in the success of
Russian agents.

Their stop at the hardware store was without inci-
dent. Although Illych was not anxious to expose
himself, he nevertheless would not trust Mario to

buy the batteries. He selected them himself and hauled the heavy carton back to the car, placing it in the rear. He then told Mario that he must make the other purchases.

As they took up their drive through the noonday traffic, Illych consulted the list. Most of the requests were for articles such as candy, pocket combs and razor blades, but without exception the men demanded cigars and cigarettes.

Illych told the driver to park midway between a tobacco shop and a large general store where the sundries could be purchased.

"I will wait in the car with the motor running," he said, "in case we have to leave in a hurry."

Mario was to get the miscellaneous articles first and not to take too much time doing so. The cigarettes and cigars were more important, for they helped to calm the men in a crisis. Illych had handled his men far too long not to realize the importance of keeping them happy with small personal privileges.

In the matter of minutes Mario emerged from the general store. After glancing up and down the street, he walked to the car, opened the rear door and stacked his bundles on the floor. He then sauntered down the street to the tobacco shop.

Illych twisted the rearview mirror so that he could see the entrance to the tobacco shop. After the driver entered, the leader sat back and rehearsed his future plans. This would be the last pause before they were on their way. He had to admit that the decadent enemy had blocked them quite well, but he would find a way to fool them! He might be a smalltime leader now, but his heroic exploits would soon be proclaimed in every corner of the Soviet! Perhaps he would be rewarded by a post of singular honor!

In the midst of his dreams, Illych suddenly became aware that it was taking the driver an extremely long time to make a few purchases. Always suspicious, he had a feeling that bad luck—a condition reserved for himself—might have descended to thwart his well-laid plans. This he would not tolerate; not at the moment of glory! Mario was a dolt! Those stupid men could do nothing without strong leadership.

Resolutely he climbed from the car and sauntered down the street. He peered into the shop door. There was his comrade standing near a counter and obviously waiting for a salesman to return. Illych was enraged by his revealing nervous manner. He went in and, completely ignoring Mario, stepped into an empty phone booth and closed the door. He dialed an imaginary number, meanwhile keeping an eye peeled on the scene outside the booth.

The heat in the booth became oppressive, and Illych's glasses were so fogged with steam from his breathing that he could scarcely see. He took them off and started wiping the lenses with a handkerchief. Even without his spectacles, he could see Mario taking the packages and hurrying toward the door.

Illych breathed a sigh of relief. The delay had gotten on his nerves more than he cared to admit. Though he was a brave man in an open battle, Illych became uneasy when danger was unnamed threats lurking in the corners. He sighed. But soon he would be free of all these foolish doubts. Blithely Illych pushed open the door of the booth, just as a man entered the store.

Chapter 13

IDENTIFICATION

WHILE hope of escape was welling in Illych, a vast, invisible net, with strands still shredded and untied, started to pull together. Thorne burst into the apartment and found Kincaid stretched out on the couch in a position that suggested he had settled down for a long, uninterrupted sleep.

"Wake up, Jack!" the sergeant shouted. "We've found them. Silver Chief has done it again!"

Kincaid was completely awake in the matter of seconds; he was fully alert, with no yawning or fumbling of speech. He glanced at his watch, raised himself from the couch and flipped his lighter, all in one series of smooth motions. He was a businesslike machine, firing questions at the sergeant.

"Found who? Where? Have you called anybody?" he demanded.

Thorne shook his head.

"Well, let me call Headquarters. . . . But keep on talking." Kincaid spun the dial, then asked, "Are you sure you spotted the guys we're after?"

"If I'm not, Silver Chief is," Thorne returned. "And he *knows*, Jack."

Kincaid looked a trifle skeptical as he glanced from Thorne to Silver Chief and back to Thorne again. "O.K., Sergeant, what happened?"

Briefly Thorne recounted the events in the park, including the fact that he actually had not seen much, since Chief had contacted the enemy. Thorne did, however, state positive identification of the dog.

"I ought to know that one," the sergeant said, "even though it was only through a car window. The beast almost deprived me of my leg up North."

"You do have reason to remember him," Kincaid admitted.

"Besides, Silver Chief would not have attacked the dog so furiously if he had no cause," the sergeant assured his friend.

Jack listened until someone on the other end of the line spoke, then he announced himself.

"Kincaid here. First—is there anything to report at that end? No . . . Well we *have*. Sergeant Thorne's dog tangled with an animal in the park this morning. A fight resulted. Thorne recognized the beast as the one that accompanied the Russian agents in Canada. Putting the pieces together, I am willing to assume that his identification is correct.

"I want you to alert every agent on the job by word of mouth. No phoning. I want no leaks. Double-check all tips, no matter how trivial. No radios for reporting. We'll be down shortly to see if anything comes in. That is all. Good-by."

Kincaid hung up the phone and ground out his cigarette in the ash tray.

"Come on, Pete, let's get cleaned up a little and

get down to Headquarters. They can rustle up some breakfast for us there."

"Righto, I'll be with you in a second. Heaven knows I'm anxious to be off, and so is Chief. He's as alert as a fox now that he's tasted blood. Into the bathroom with me, fellow, I'll clean up your whiskers while we're at it."

Headquarters, as Kincaid called it, was not what the name implied in the usual sense, but consisted of three rooms in a downtown office building, furnished with a few well-worn maple desks and half a dozen creaky chairs. The windows were dirty, and one unshaded bulb dangled from the ceiling to light the room. Battered, butt-filled ash trays littered the desks, fighting for room between numerous telephones. Several men in shirt sleeves, their collars unloosed, were doing nothing but picking up receivers. One man sat at a large desk, a map of metropolitan San Francisco spread before him. Whenever a message was taken, the agent called a number, then the man would make a check on the map, a notation of the time, the source and location of the call.

What at first glance appeared to be disorganized bedlam, was, in fact, a well-run answering service and nerve center for every agent on duty in the city. Thorne was amazed at the manpower the FBI was able to muster at a given spot in an emergency. Accustomed to working alone and assuming the responsibility for solving problems as he thought best, he could still see the advantage of being able to assemble many trained men for a case as important as the one they were now trying to solve.

Thorne had never quite become used to the vast-
ness of cities. The buildings gave him a feeling of
being shut in. Having witnessed Chief's happiness in
the park, Thorne was sure that his dog felt the same,
that he too longed to be back in the wide-open spaces
and the freedom of the great silent North. On the
other hand, it would have been difficult to picture
Jack Kincaid removed from the activity and bustle
about him.

The minute Jack thrust his lean, hard body into
a room, he seemed to take over the situation. Heads
turned toward him, voices were stilled and cigarettes
were poised in mid-air.

"Morning, everybody!" Kincaid called. "This is
Sergeant Thorne of the Royal Canadian Mounted
Police, and his dog Silver Chief. You know why he
is here, so help the sergeant with anything he needs.
You have all been briefed on what took place this
morning, so we are now going on the assumption
that the enemy is nearby."

The men all glanced with friendly interest at
Thorne and Silver Chief.

"It is a very heartening fact," Kincaid continued,
"that the sergeant and his dog recently delivered a
murderer up in Canada, one who is doubtlessly a
member of the gang of foreign spies. Let's show him
how we operate down here. We must continue
until we have run the suspects down. I am going out
to brief as many men at their posts as possible.
Thorne will remain, in case anything turns up. If
any clues are reported, the sergeant and his dog will
be taken to the call post pronto. . . . Understand?"

Before Kincaid left, the sergeant beckoned to him.

"See you for a minute, Jack? I have a small suggestion, and if you do not mind . . ."

"Of course I don't mind. You're here to make
suggestions. If our outfit never slipped up, there
would not be any criminals running around loose.
Shoot!"

"Well, it's like this . . . When Silver Chief sinks his
fangs into tough hide, something is bound to give.
There's no way of telling how bad he hurt the other
dog, but from the blood and pieces of hide I cleaned
off his jaws, it was a good-sized bite. Maybe the owner
of the other dog does not know about patching up
animals, so what about covering the veterinarians'
offices?"

"Very good idea, Pete. I'll phone to the local police.
That's a job their force can handle in less than an
hour, without disclosing too much information. And
look, I'll phone you personally every half-hour. I'll
use our code word. No one around here knows it."

Kincaid ducked out of the door and down the
corridor before Thorne could answer.

Thorne spent the rest of the morning in routine criminal detection, watching each report that
came from animal hospitals, and sorting out the
value of other messages. No dog resembling the description of Chelkar had been treated, and none of
the other reports seemed relevant to the case.

Silver Chief was restless; he paced back and forth
sniffing trouser legs, corners, chairs. He was tense
to be back on the scent of the enemy.

Shortly after noon a call came from downtown San
Francisco and one of the men brought it excitedly to
Thorne.

"Sergeant," he said, "there's a report from one of our agents who is checking tobacco stores in this district . . ." He pointed on the map to a three-block area near the Market Street ferries. "He states that two men drove up to a store a few minutes ago and parked. Our white wing noticed the car because he was on the alert for customers going into tobacco shops, and also because this car is the same color and type you described."

"I see," Thorne said. "But tell me, what's a white wing?"

"Sorry, Sergeant. I forgot you're not familar with some of our lingo. A white wing is a street cleaner. It is a disguise. Almost all of our men use disguises when necessary. TV repairmen, telephone line riggers, milkmen—anything the public takes for granted. This man Collins uses his broom so well that even the regular cleaners think he's one of them."

The sergeant smiled. "What else did the report say?"

"It seems that the salesman in the shop is stalling because one of the men from this car is asking for Gold-Flake cigarettes. We've asked shops to report any purchases of this brand. Besides, our white wing seems to think the customer is more than a little rattled by being asked to wait. It may mean nothing, but how about having a look?"

"Sounds like a good idea. Especially the coincidence of the car *and* the cigarettes. Let's go."

Silver Chief had risen to his feet and stood in front of the door before Thorne could even button on his jacket.

Both he and his master had been on many perilous rides, in many strange and weird contraptions in their days together, but nothing could match the ride their driver gave them through the crowded downtown section of San Francisco, threading through traffic, weaving in and out like a greyhound. The agent drove with superb nonchalance, as though the pace was his everyday rate of speed. With a squeal of brakes he drew up to the curb and opened the door for Thorne.

"Just hop around the corner, Sergeant, and down to the middle of the block. You'll see a candy, newspaper and cigar store, with an awning overhead. Walk right in, but if I were you I'd keep your gun handy. We have an 'A and D' warning on the wanted men."

"A and D . . . what is that?"

"Armed and dangerous, Sergeant. Good hunting, sir. I'll be standing by with the dog."

"Thanks." Thorne got out of the car and walked slowly around the corner. He could see Silver Chief through the window of the car, as the agent slowly turned the corner after him.

As he was about to enter the store, the sergeant caught sight of a small, stooped man lighting a cigarette. He stood between two parked cars, leaning on the push handle of his cart. He was dressed in an ill-fitting white uniform, and he wore an expression of timid humility. The sergeant had to admit to himself that he never would have believed an agent of the FBI lurked behind that innocent-looking disguise.

As Thorne entered the shop, a nervous, jittery man with a package under his arm turned from the coun-

ter. Approaching the door, he looked directly at
Thorne. Not the slightest trace of recognition passed
between the two. The excited, taut feeling in the
sergeant's stomach relaxed, and he withdrew his hand
from the pocket where he had clutched his revolver.

Thorne let the man proceed, while he remained
to buy a package of cigarettes. While waiting for his
change he turned. A man stepped out of the phone
booth near the door—his glasses were off and he was
polishing them with a handkerchief. The stranger
suddenly looked up. Bewildered anxiety flashed
across his face—that ugly, familiar face with the same
badly crossed eye!

Illych moved with the quickness of a cat through
the door and out into the sunshine. As Thorne followed, Mario dropped his packages and enveloped
the sergeant in huge, powerful arms. Squirming and
panting, the sergeant tried to free himself, as Illych
dashed up the street to the standing limousine.
Grimly Mario held on, until the white wing, aban-
doning his air of timidity, crossed the sidewalk in a
bound and threw himself on Thorne's assailant.

By the time the sergeant was released he saw the
limousine pull rapidly from the curb out into a
stream of traffic, its rear tires screaming as the driver
pressed the accelerator to the floor.

Feeling quite helpless for a moment, Thorne was
nevertheless happy to notice that the small coupe
which had been innocently parked, sprang from the
traffic line in pursuit of the fast-disappearing limousine. With the help of the agent who had brought
him there and with Silver Chief on the trail, perhaps
all was not yet lost!

Again Thorne turned to the struggling men. Mario had managed to lock his long arms around the white wing's body, perhaps the only grip he knew. Thorne grasped one of Mario's wrists and bent it back, and yet back behind the Russian's body, until he could no longer bear the pain, and with a groan he released the white wing and fell to the sidewalk.

The agent immediately pulled out a pair of handcuffs from his pocket, snapped one bracelet on Mario's arm, the other on his own. He yanked his prisoner up roughly just as another coupe drew up alongside the curb. Kincaid sprang through the gathering throng and shouldered his way directly to Thorne.

"What happened? Tell me quick, Peter," he demanded.

Chapter 14

MURDER AGAIN!

Like a cyclone, Illych burst through the back door into the hide-out, his face dead white and contorted with rage and frustration. The men who had been lounging around the kitchen sprang up, knowing that something had gone wrong.

The leader stalked through the kitchen and into the radio room without stopping. With maniacal fury he tore into the radio equipment that remained, ripping and clawing it with all his might. He bellowed out orders at the top of his voice. The kitchen erupted into furious activity. Five minutes later, after completely wrecking every piece of equipment, Illych strode into the kitchen and held up his hand for silence.

"The American agents have definitely found out that we are in San Francisco! I have just barely escaped from their trap. They have taken Comrade Mario prisoner and will no doubt submit him to their well-known tortures. Stelka!" he yelled.

"Yes, Comrade Illych," Stelka replied.

"It is useless for us to attempt to escape from San Francisco with even the small pieces of the ore sample I am carrying. The enemy is too close on our trail. My original plan to ship out as an able-bodied seaman for Hong Kong is useless, as I would now be easily recognized.

"Even now I am wasting too much time in discussion. All of our original plans are too risky. This has been clearly demonstrated."

"I agree with you completely, Comrade," Stelka answered. "What is the alternate proposition?"

Illych looked coldly at his questioner. "That I will reveal to you when I am ready." Then, with deliberate malice, he turned toward the other men. "Lackvief, *you* will go with me as pilot. . . . And you, Richiensky, a member of the party. . . . Boris, did you contact our man in San Pedro to arrange for a meeting tonight?"

"Yes, Comrade Illych. The hour of the meeting is as planned."

"Good. After that we will return to our northern rendezvous and secure the crate with the large samples of ore. This time we will not fail. The fresh batteries you asked for, Boris, are on the back seat of the car. Be sure to test them. We must be able to contact Siberia."

As if he had not noticed the leader's slight of him, Stelka inquired: "Will we be returning to Dawson City, Comrade?"

"Our plans are not yet decided," snapped Illych. "I am sure that is where they picked up our trail. Our contact north is made by a different route. Any other questions?"

No one spoke. Each man knew his job.

"Good. Then you will disperse immediately. Every one of you knows where to go and what duties to perform. If there is any doubt, however, speak to me before we leave. We must have no more slip-ups. Our mission *must* be accomplished.

"I will not say 'good luck' to my men. We do not admit that chance has any part in success. Bad luck, yes. There is a penalty for that, remember."

Even after the men had started to move about in preparation for departure, Stelka remained at the side of his leader. Though his face had a somewhat questioning expression, his eyes were resolute.

"What happened, Comrade Illych?" he asked. "It is curious that we were traced here so quickly. We have been told so often that our enemies are lazy, slothful fools. Could we possibly have lulled our-selves into believing that which is not so?"

"Be still, Stelka. I do not care for this line of ques-tioning. It seems to me that you have a sneaking admiration for these bourgeois. I have no time for discussion with you now. If I have been followed, it will be only a matter of minutes before a house-to-house search is made, and less than an hour before we will be traced here."

Illych watched the men at their appointed tasks, his eyes almost invisible behind the thick lenses. He checked every last-minute detail to assure their safe departure.

"Were there any messages from Washington?" he asked suddenly.

One of the men spoke in a low, quick voice.

"Yes, Comrade Illych. Boris received a message. He was informed that Feodor made contact with the Canadian, but his attempt was thwarted by a huge white dog which attacked in defense of his master."

Illych clenched his fists till the knuckles stood out white.

"That accursed dog again! I would crush him to death with my bare hands if possible. He is an omen."

"Yes, Comrade," the man agreed. "But listen now. There were two messages from the Embassy. One said you will have to proceed according to your own judgment and that you should redouble your efforts. The ore is assuming more and more world-wide importance. Russia must know why. Within possibilities, call upon any resources at their command."

Illych grunted. "Possibilities are getting extremely limited. Anything else."

"Just one somewhat vague bit of information, stating that the secret ore contains ultraviolet as well as infrared properties. A full report of these will be brought here by courier."

"That all sounds very interesting," Illych commented, "but it means absolutely nothing to me. Whatever the properties are, we will be gone before the courier arrives. Our one and only problem is to see that the crate and its contents reach Soviet territory. First things first! Between here and our next rendezvous, I must somehow get word to Russia or to an agent in Siberia.

"All of you, out now. I will follow in a moment with Stelka and the dog. We will check the house and see that nothing is left behind. Depart in twos or small groups. That is less suspicious-looking."

When the men had gone, Illych went to the upper floors to check, while Stelka went over the first two floors. Methodically and with extreme care Stelka searched closets and corners. He was kneeling to peer beneath a radiator when his leader returned. He stood before Stelka with wide-planted feet, and in a silence that seemed to throb. Stelka rose slowly to gaze into the cold, expressionless face of his leader.

"Comrade Stelka, there are a few last matters I wish to speak of before leaving."

Though Illych's words came out of his mouth like hard pellets of hail, Stelka answered easily.

"Of course, Comrade Illych."

"You have been a fine man to work with, Comrade Stelka. You are a pilot of airplanes, a man of intelligence, with an admirable record."

"Thank you."

"Yes, as a former officer in the Heroes of the October Revolution Division, your record was outstanding on the Western Front when fighting the Nazi beasts. Your recommendations were of the highest, and in most ways you have fulfilled them."

"Thank you again."

Comrade Illych continued:

"And you may be certain that I will recommend you for loyalty, up to a certain point . . ."

"At what point did I fail in loyalty?" Stelka demanded.

"Well, as I suggested to you awhile ago, I have sensed some sneaking admiration in you for—well let us call it certain qualities of our enemies. Don't interrupt, Stelka. As you know, I have had many things on my mind. But this morning when Chelkar returned bloody and wounded, something stirred in my subconscious mind. Something I did not like."

"What was that, Comrade?"

"It came to me that you, of all my trusted agents,

had disobeyed direct orders. A certain Canadian officer was supposed to have been shot to death. Perhaps for a moment this morning my friendship for you made me wish that this order had been carried out. But your manner, Stelka, the way you tried to cover up. . . . You know that Canadian to be alive!"

"That is your belief, Comrade."

"Silence!" Illych roared. "Were it not for your softness, we might now have achieved our mission. Then there would only be the murder of a Canadian pilot, and Igam held as his murderer. As it is, they have nearly run us to earth. And all because you have disobeyed! You were ordered to kill that man. You did not shoot to kill. Why?"

Stelka spoke quietly, yet with assurance.

"Comrade Illych, there is much to be admired about you. You do your duty as you see it. You do it with ability. You are a forceful man, but one weakness that will bring your ultimate downfall is lack of imagination. For you there is only one method, the shortest and most direct. This can be admirable and oftentimes a successful approach. If anything gets in your path, it is destroyed. This also is a fine method of getting results. But it does not take into account the human factor. Men are human beings, Illych, not machines as you and the Communist Party like to think. Men think and feel and believe. It is this that you forget. It is what makes you underestimate the enemy.

"You are right. I did disobey you. Directly and with a clear mind. You may or may not know that Igam was a sergeant gunner in my regiment on the Western Front.

"In the battle before Moscow, Igam fought with such outstanding valor that he was given a lieutenant's commission in the field. Twice with his battery he saved our regiment from certain annihilation from the attacking Nazi hordes. Personally he fired his cannon until the barrel became white-hot and melted the bore, to keep back the attackers. Igam was a fine, brave man, Illych, yet you abandoned him in the North woods, without hope, or mercy.

"I am well aware of the stakes in the game we are playing, but destroying merely for the sake of destroying is not part of our plan, nor of my code. To kill or be killed is a different matter. There my record speaks for itself.

"As to the man we fought in the snow. My principle was the same for him. He was a brave man and fought a good fight against us. He believed in what he thought right, as we do. You had clubbed him into insensibility; there was every chance he would die from freezing.

"Again I take you back to the days of the last war. When our defense of Moscow turned into an offense, and we began to attack the Nazis and started our long march to Berlin, we captured many thousand Nazi soldiers and officers. As you know, the Heroes of the October Revolution Division was a Guards Division and fought in the thick of the worst battle, and always against the picked divisions of the German Army. We had occasion many times to meet with the captured German officers. They too were brave men, Illych. In a way you would not grasp, we understood them when they told us they were sick almost to death of the senseless bloodletting. They fought for an ideal and died for it, as did so many millions of the sons of Russia. I admired these men, as they admired me, for you see, Illych, we were brothers of war.

"It was the same with the man in the woods. He fought honorably and well. I would not kill this man, as I hope he would not kill me if the situation were reversed.

"I can see by the look in your face, Illych, you neither understand nor care what I am saying."

Illych ignored Stelka's question. "You admit that you disobeyed me," he snapped.

"Of course; you have heard me."

"For this, Comrade Stelka, you must die!"

"You call me Comrade. All right. So then I must die. But hear me, you too will die from your own stupidity!"

The implacable frozen mask that had been Illych's face was now reddened and bloated with fury. His hand slid slowly into a pocket . . .

Stelka lunged forward, but as he did, the room exploded with sound as two shots rang out. Chelkar sprang, growling, to his feet.

Without a cry, Stelka slumped to the floor, and neither the dog he had cared for nor the man he had counted as a friend gave his body a second look.

Illych stepped gingerly over the fallen man as he grasped Chelkar's leash and yanked him through the door.

The house became grim and silent. Gunpowder fumes hung in the close air of the kitchen as though there was no other place for them to go.

Chapter 15

THE GET-AWAY

DESPITE the confused excitement at the tobacco shop, Kincaid lost no time in getting the wheels of the law spinning again. When a city police car drove up to the curb, he got in and beckoned Thorne to join him. At first the officers were a little startled at Kincaid's abrupt manner, but they quietly handed over their two-way telephone receiver when he requested it.

As Jack spoke to Headquarters, the look of tense concentration left his face. He snapped a few quick orders and then returned the phone to the man in the front seat. He next spoke to the city officers.

"I want you to take that man you see over there with his prisoner to FBI Headquarters. He is Collins, one of our agents. And I must ask you not to speak of this arrest to anyone. It is a Government case, and the prisoner is an important link in an outfit we're trying to run down. If he demands a lawyer or voices his rights about citizenship, tell him he's being held under the Enemy Alien Act. Our agent will handle the rest."

Both men nodded in agreement.

"And I'd appreciate it," Kincaid continued, "if you'd send somebody to pick up that barrel and broom. See it over there between the two cars? For all I know it may be city property."

The driver spoke for both. "Sure, sir. We were sent down here on 'Emergency 28' call, which means it's Federal business. So anything you say. We'll have the Department of Sanitation send a truck over and pick up the props."

"Right . . . Thanks, and you will forget the whole . . ."

"Can't even remember getting a call, sir." The driver grinned as Thorne and Kincaid stepped out of the car and re-entered a smaller four-door sedan driven by a man in civilian clothes.

As soon as Kincaid had seated himself in the rear, he spoke to the driver.

"O.K., Bob, turn it on loud; we may as well hear it in the clear, direct . . ."

"Yes, sir," the driver answered, as he leaned over and switched on the radio-telephone receiver. A voice crackled out into the car, well defined, though coming from far off.

". . . Simmons again. . . . The car ahead went through Oakland after we crossed the bridge. It was driven directly through the city and headed for the dock area. We turned left at 45th and Gorman just as he pulled into a garage in a factory district. The driver closed the garage door as soon as he entered. I left the dog in the car and walked past the door. There are no windows, and only the one door facing the street. The building is a block away from the docks, but there is an alley separating it from the dock buildings . . . I am standing by, and have let the dog out of the car. Instead of circling the entire block, the dog cut through an alley and is now returning. Am standing by for further suggestions."

Thorne felt a great load lifted from his mind when he heard that Silver Chief was unharmed and on the job.

Meanwhile, Jack switched back to the broadcast unit in the car.

"Hello, Simmons. . . . Jack Kincaid here. . . . Fine work. Stay where you are and keep on the alert. The man is A and D. We are on our way. . . . Also, you'd better get the dog back in the car. The men we're after would like to put a slug in him for keeps. . . . Acknowledge. . . . Over."

"Simmons to Kincaid. . . . Roger. . . . Over."

They had already headed into the approaches of the Bay Bridge to Oakland. Thorne looked in astonishment at the size and length of the span over which they were driving.

Jack noticed the sergeant's admiration. "Some bridge, isn't it, Pete? It never fails to get me, either. Supposed to be one of the greatest engineering feats man has ever produced. I can well believe it."

"So can I," Thorne agreed.

They drove through Oakland in silence and soon arrived at the factory district designated by Simmons' call. Quietly the driver brought them up beside the coupe parked near the corner.

When Silver Chief recognized Thorne as one of the new arrivals, his tail wagged furiously and brushed like a huge fan across the good-natured face of Simmons.

After they had all alighted from the cars, Kincaid looked about to appraise the general situation. He could see that the whole area, consisting of a series of warehouses, was almost deserted.

"Thorne, you and Chief come with me," Jack said. "Simmons, it might be a good idea for you to stay here and cover us, just in case. And you, Mac, drive around the block and through that alley. See if there is anything we should know about. I'm going to try to get through that garage door somehow."

They approached the sliding steel garage doors warily. They could see that a smaller door had been cut in the big door. On this was a large new lock.

"Hey, Simmons, have you got the standard key set? This is a typical everyday lock. I think a basic skeleton key will do unless they've put a rig on from the inside."

"Sure, Jack." The agent unlocked the glove compartment of his car and took out a ring with some fifty keys on it, which he handed to Kincaid.

"I guess you don't have much use for these things in Canada, Pete," Kincaid said. "These are basic skeleton keys for about ninety-five per cent of all locks used in the United States. Very handy little tools. They're in great demand by many shady characters."

"I don't doubt it," Thorne replied. "We used to practice with them in training. But in Canada most doors are left open. The locked ones have a way of yielding to the Mounties . . ."

Jack gave the Mountie an amused look as he picked three keys from the ring and inserted one of them into the lock. On the second try the lock clicked, and the door started to swing open. Kincaid withdrew the key and handed the ring back to Simmons.

"Simmons, why don't you park your car directly in front of this garage doorway to block it? And you come along with us. That key ring may come in handy. Come on, Thorne, let's find out what goes on in here."

"Right . . ."

Thorne followed Jack's example. He too drew his revolver, first pushing the safety release to "off." Kincaid led the way, followed by Thorne with Silver Chief obediently at heel. Simmons brought up the rear.

As far as they could see, the gloomy interior was empty, except for a large familiar-looking limousine that had been parked some distance from the door. Cautiously Jack moved to the side of the car and peered down on the floor. Finding nothing there, he walked around to feel the radiator. It was still warm.

He turned and spoke in low tones to the sergeant.

"You go one way around the walls; I'll go the other with Simmons. Watch out for trap doors or secret panels. This whole setup has a phony look. It is obviously a blind, and it may take awhile to find the proper exit."

Thorne grinned. "I don't think it will take us long," he said. "This is a problem for Silver Chief." Opening the limousine door, he snapped his fingers.

"Get 'em, Chief. At 'em, boy!"

Chief sniffed at the car door for a moment, lowered his nose to the concrete floor of the garage and then moved to a corner of the building. There a huge packing case, its stenciled label indicating it had been used to crate a piano, was jammed against the wall. Though dust nearly an inch deep covered the wood, Chief stood stock-still at the spot, waiting for the men to come up.

"See how simple it is," the sergeant said. "Chief can smell a booby trap it might take us hours to find!"

Jack patted the dog casually as he scanned the box. "I never denied that Chief is a great policeman. Come on, let's get this crate open."

For at least five minutes they examined the box without success. Suddenly Simmons gave a low whistle, at the same time pointing to a heavily barred window. The thick dust on the pane blotted out all light, making the window almost unnoticeable. A wire also dangled from above, almost obscured because of its coloring.

"Uh-huh," Simmons said. "I figured this contraption to be some kind of trap door with an electrical unit to operate it. The sides of the box are too well finished to conceal an outer spring. A button must be hidden somewhere. I'll show you how to do it and save time."

He reached into his hip pocket and pulled out a comb-and-nail-file set from a leather case. Withdrawing the file, he reached up to the wire that disappeared behind the box. As he was rasping the covering to expose the wire itself, the others stiffened to attention as two loud, distinct explosions came from some point beyond the box. Kincaid was the first to be galvanized into action.

"Hurry up, Simmons. Do something quick. Those were shots we just heard. Something's happening."

"Here you go, Jack. Stand back. I'm either going to short this arrangement out or make contact with the file. Something ought to give."

He placed the nail file across the two exposed wires encased in the covering. Silently and easily the door of the box swung open. Simmons was the first to peer in.

"See, what did I tell you? A simple contact switch. See those sawed-off nailheads all along the box? They're nothing but fakes. Be careful. They may have a mine rigged, or a trip alarm. I'll go ahead and . . ."

Jack interrupted him. "No you don't, Simmons. I'll take the lead. You stay and cover us from the rear."

Now it was Thorne's time to interrupt.

"Wait a minute, Jack. This is the stuff that Silver Chief and I are best at . . . Chief first, then me, then you. Let's not argue. C'mon."

Before there was time to protest, Thorne had called Chief to heel. Both stepped into the gloom of the box, from which a flight of steps led downward. At the bottom of the steps Thorne could see a tunnel with a rounded roof, but a flat floor, which led away from the building in the direction of the water front. The sergeant strode quickly forward, gun in hand, alert and ready. Silver Chief preceded him, stalking along, nose in air.

Jack, behind Thorne, kept looking up as they walked along.

"We're going under the alley back of the building," he said. "This looks like an old abandoned sewage viaduct. Too well built to be here on a temporary basis. The gang probably stumbled on it accidentally and used it for their get-away. We're headed in the direction of the Bay right now."

Another twenty feet ahead, a flight of steps could be seen cut into the left side of the culvert, leading upward. A dim bulb burned in a socket that was suspended above the steps. Silver Chief sprang ahead of Thorne and up the stairs, his nose lowered almost to the treads. They found another door with a spring lock, similar to the one on the door of the garage.

Kincaid took out his key ring and prepared to check the lock number. At the same instant Silver Chief placed a paw against the door firmly, with a gesture of impatience. Surprisingly enough it swung open slightly. Thorne and Kincaid exchanged glances. The lock had not even been fastened. With extreme caution the two men entered a basement, where they could see another light burning dimly on the far wall of the littered room.

Silver Chief, with unerring instinct, guided them to another flight of stairs leading up from the basement. Just as Thorne started up after his dog, Kincaid clutched his arm. They both listened. A faint, whining moan sounded from above.

"There's someone in pain up there," the sergeant cried. "Hurry!"

Tossing aside caution, he raced up the stairs and into the kitchen, gun thrust menacingly. Another anguished moan made him turn his eyes toward a figure on the floor. Kincaid burst into the room just at that moment.

"That is what we heard, Jack." Though they were obviously alone with the figure, Thorne could not help whispering. In a few strides he was leaning over the crumpled form of Stelka, staring down into his face.

"This is one of the men I fought with in Canada, Jack. Look at his nose. It's still not healed from the punch I gave him. We got the poor devil, but it seems his Comrade got him first!"

As they gazed down at the wounded man, Silver Chief roamed around the room, his hackles rising from telltale scent of the enemy.

Stelka lay very still, his breath coming in jerky, uneven gasps. The front of his body was a mass of blood, still oozing and unclotted. Stelka tried to open his eyes and he made a superhuman effort to speak. Bloody saliva dribbled from between his lips, in this effort not to lose consciousness.

Kincaid leaned over to help the dying man, but it was too late. Stelka opened his eyes and spoke two words with crazed ferocity, "Comrade Illych . . ." He was unable to go on. With an agonized shudder his body went limp; Stelka was dead.

Jack was the first to speak.

"I can never quite get used to seeing men die. It makes no difference if they are good or bad. Life is our greatest gift and so few of us are prepared for what might come."

It was the first time in their association that Thorne had heard his friend become philosophical

or sentimental. But Jack soon returned to his usual
active self.

"God rest his soul," he said, "but now we have
work to do. You are positive, then, of your identification?"

"I am. And about the man in the tobacco shop as
well. Why do you suppose these two quarreled? What
is it all about?"

"We'll never know unless we keep on looking."

Kincaid continued his search, peering into the bedroom, where smashed equipment was scattered all
about. The telephone had been yanked loose from
the wall with what seemed unnecessary thoroughness.

"We might try something else," Thorne said. He
reached into his pocket and pulled out the piece of
glass that had been given to him in the Virginia laboratory. First he looked at Stelka and then he glanced
about the room.

"Look, Jack," he said excitedly, "this is the weirdest
effect I've ever seen. That scientist really knew what
he was talking about."

Kincaid pulled out his own glass and stared
through it.

"It's fantastic, isn't it, Pete? Do you notice anything unusual about the dead man?"

"Nothing; no ultraviolet green shows on him, even
though it is all over the room."

"That's right, Pete. That means someone else has
a sample of the ore. If you look through this glass
you could follow him as easily as in an old-fashioned
paper chase we used to play when we were kids."

Thorne grinned. "It's funny that you should men-
tion that. We used to play the same thing up North

in the woods, only we didn't use paper; we used
Indian signs."

Jack spoke now in an undertone: "There is so
much evidence of the ore around, it is hard to decide
where to start."

Thorne answered him. "Don't worry about these
scientific gadgets. We still have Silver Chief."

Kincaid snapped his fingers delightedly.

"You're so right, Sergeant. They sure did a complete job of wrecking this place." Both men looked
at the shambles. "Even smashed the light and water
meter," Kincaid continued. "Typical Russian thoroughness. Always great on all the little things; always
miss and slip up on the big ones. It seems to me, as
I study these people, that they just don't seem to be
able to grasp whole situations. I guess it's because
they are so used to having a higher-up do their thinking for them. Here we have smashed light and water
meters. But why do they kill a valuable agent, such
as this man obviously was? It's senseless. No pattern;
just undefined efficiency."

"True," the sergeant agreed. "But whoever shot
him can't be too far away. Remember, we heard the
shots less than ten minutes ago, and you notice he did
not come through the tunnel."

Just then Silver Chief tried to convey a message of
his own to Thorne and Kincaid. As he walked around
a large basket on the floor, he let out a series of
growls.

"Ah!" said Thorne. "Obviously the spot where the
monster Chelkar slept." He went over to Silver Chief
and spoke to him. "Not the dog, fellow!" He led
Chief over toward the steps to the basement. "There,

Chief. Get him, boy." Thorne gave his dog a smack
on the rump. Away the dog went, tail up, nose graz-
ing the floor. Instead of returning to the basement,
however, Chief circled the room again, the scent
taking him to an alcove behind the kitchen where
the icebox was kept. When he sniffed at an outside
door, Kincaid threw back the twin locks.

"Seems to be this way. Chief looks as if he's on a
hot scent."

The door led out into a grubby narrow back yard
that obviously had once been a garden, but now was
a weed-grown rubbish heap. Chief bounded through
a gate in a high board fence at the end of the yard
before either man could reach there.

A decrepit old dock extended into the Bay for
perhaps fifty feet. Its boards were rotted and many
of the planks had been washed away. Thorne and
Kincaid hurried to the end of the dock. All around
them they could see the huge modern warehouses,
loading docks, cranes, and equipment of industrial
Oakland. Across the Bay, San Francisco shimmered
in the afternoon haze like a fairy city floating on a
soft, magic carpet.

Sergeant Thorne was the first to spot a ladder
leading to the water. He climbed down and peered
under the dark water-stained dock.

"Here's your answer, Jack. They had a boat under
here. It evidently was slung up from the water on
davits, just like a lifeboat. Release two ropes and
she'd be launched, ready to go. I'll bet they had some
sort of old planking across the front of the dock here
to conceal the boat. They could easily kick it loose
in just such an emergency.

"... Quite a setup. I think I can see where the back davit is slung. Walk back along the dock. There, right about there." Thorne climbed up the short ladder and stood on the dock about three feet from the end. "Here's where the front davit is."

He paced off the distance to the spot where Kincaid was standing. Then he measured off the width. Next he leaned over the side of the dock and saw that the water was washing close to the top of the high-tide line.

"Looks to me about high tide, Jack. The dock is no more than four feet from mean high water. That would make their boat about three feet high if they kept it slung out of the water. Roughly, we'll want to look out for a runabout or boat, probably very fast. . . . About thirteen feet long, six feet wide, with little or no canopy or covering."

"Very good, Pete. Sounds like what they'd probably have. A fast Chris-Craft, or some other type fairly common around the Bay. It's like looking for a needle in a haystack with the hundreds of miles of shore line around the Bay area. But we've got to see what we can do. Let's hurry back to a phone. I'll get the Metropolitan Harbor Police. They are a crackerjack outfit and know more about this kind of thing than we can ever hope to."

An hour later, back at Headquarters, Sergeant Thorne sat quietly as he watched Kincaid again marshal various branches of the law into the search for the missing speedboat.

Again came the plodding, careful routine that spells the doom of so many criminals—the patient

search and follow-up of the slightest clue. Checking
rumors, checking known facts, checking everything
connected with boats and their owners, or any other
possible information that could be of help.

By nightfall the search was organized, but there
was not one single traceable clue to work on. The
boat and its occupants had simply vanished.

Until midnight Kincaid directed the search, trying
to weigh every possible method of escape. He had
men check every plane leaving the airport. Every
train was checked; even the commuter trains on the
Peninsula were gone over.

All boats, large and small, leaving the harbor were
searched carefully. Nothing was left to chance. All
strange aircraft were made to identify themselves.

The Strategic Air Command was again alerted.
The Coast Guard and the Navy were asked to be
especially vigilant. Night falling about San Francisco
had thousands of eyes, all searching, looking, thinking. Radar, the sleepless eye, scanned the oceans and
the skies; radio and telephone kept contact with the
human eyes peering, looking, searching. But the boat
and its occupants could not be found.

The next morning Peter Thorne awoke to see
Kincaid smoking furiously as he talked on the phone.
He could see that Silver Chief as always was ready to
begin the day as soon as he saw his master awaken.

All that day and the night following, reports sifted
in from every corner of the United States and Canada.
The search was never-ending. Each report was
checked, verified and then discarded. Not a trace of

the boat could be found. The Russian Consulate was asked if it knew anything of such a boat, but the answer was bland, polite, and final! "Nothing."

The following day and night were much like the previous ones. Thorne felt a helpless rage creeping over him. A week had passed since the grim morning in that North Canadian woods. However, he realized that the finest minds in the world were working feverishly to help him and Kincaid.

Jack was a relentless dynamo of energy. He moved like an incessant wound-up gadget, giving orders like an automatic gun, listening, weighing, and finally making decisions with the speed and precision of an adding machine. But in spite of their efforts and the energy consumed, there was still not the slightest trace of the enemy.

On the third night of the vigil Thorne sank wearily into bed. Silver Chief lay down on the floor beside him, his large eyes seeming to express sympathy to his beloved master for the unsolved mystery. Where could that boat have gotten to? Thorne's thoughts ticked on, going backward and forward, probing, but nothing could be solved. Finally, from sheer exhaustion, the sergeant fell into a troubled sleep.

The jangle of the phone brought him and Kincaid sitting bolt upright in the dark. They knew it must be important to awaken Kincaid. Jack spoke into the phone.

"Yeah? Kincaid speaking . . . Who? . . . O.K. Shoot . . . Yes . . . Yeah . . . Sure . . . That simple, hunh? Right . . . Get Simmons out of bed. We'll be there in fifteen minutes . . . G'by."

Jack slammed the receiver down on the hook and leaped out of bed with a whoop of joy. He clicked on the lights and hurried over to Thorne's bed.

"We've got 'em, Pete!" he exclaimed, shaking Thorne's hand. "We're sure we have a lead on them. Grab your stuff and pack. Fast. . . . We're off in a cloud. Hurry, and I'll tell you about it on the way down. The simplest thing in the world. Why didn't we think of it ourselves?"

Soon they were speeding down the hills of San Francisco into the center of town.

"You see, Pete, it pays off to have two governments behind you when you have some work to do. Early this evening a photo reconnaissance plane from the Strategic Air Command was flying back from Fairbanks, Alaska, to Omaha, Nebraska, on a routine training flight. Their radar picked up a ship in the channels coming into Prince Rupert, British Columbia. She was sailing in dangerous water, and when the plane dropped down to have a look, as instructed, the ship was running without lights. Also, she did not give proper recognition signals. We've had hundreds of similar reports like this one.

"When the ship pulled into Prince Rupert tonight, a Canadian Customs man went aboard to check the papers. They were all in order. It was an old beat-up freighter from San Pedro, Southern California, bound for Anchorage and Nome, with a cargo of mining supplies, which again was O.K. But the odd fact was that the skipper was an old Russian guy who barely spoke English. Said he had not acknowledged the signals as his radio was on the blink; also the electrical system for the lights had gone haywire, though everything seemed to be working around midnight when he dropped his hook.

"The Customs man made his report and we had a constable sent down to the water front to keep an eye on things. About thirty minutes ago the constable phoned that three men were rowed ashore from the freighter by a guy in a dinghy that was almost swamped by his passengers—three big men and a huge dog or a small pony.

"That was it, Peter, my boy. These are our friends. They evidently had a well-planned get-away. They raced out past the Golden Gate before we could get the alarm out, and they wallowed around in the open sea until they met with the old fellow. No wonder we never saw hide nor hair of them. Who'd think a little speedboat would wander around in the Pacific Ocean, much less that an old tramp freighter would be their home base? I'll have to hand these fellows one thing for sure: they have *some* organization!"

Kincaid burst into the Headquarters room, a smile lighting his face. "Simmons here? . . . Good. Did you call Hamilton Air Force Base? Good . . . What have they got for us this time, a B-36?"

One of the men handed Kincaid a slip of paper.

He read it and turned to Thorne. "We're going North in a small plane. They say they can't land a big fellow on the field at Fort Norman . . ."

"Fort Norman! . . ." Thorne's face betrayed his amazement.

"Yeah, Pete. I didn't have time to finish the story. One of the men went into town and found a bush pilot. They chartered his plane fifteen minutes ago, and just took off. The airport at Prince Rupert just sent us the flash. The pilot's manifest reads to Fort Norman, Northwest Territory, Mackenzie District.

"Brace up, Peter. You and Silver Chief are going home. We'll only be about three hours behind these men if we hurry. C'mon, let's get out of here. Simmons, are you ready?"

"Always, Jack."

"Thorne, Silver Chief?"

"Ready and anxious, Jack," Thorne answered with a wide smile of delight.

Chapter 16

CLOSING IN

THE plane Thorne and Kincaid had boarded from Hamilton Air Force Base droned through the still winter night, boring through the darkness as straight as an arrow northward. Up over the spiny cruel back of the Rocky Mountains, over sleeping villages and towns, roaring rivers, sleepy streams, vast prairies, and cultivated fields.

As Peter Thorne felt his heart expand with happiness, this emotion was communicated to Silver Chief, who, squatting beside his master, rested his great head on the sergeant's lap. Thorne resolved there would be no slip-up this time. They were going home!

The flight to Fort Norman was uneventful. The big U.S. Air Force plane settled on the runway, and Thorne walked into the Operations shack beside Kincaid. They were told that the bush pilot from Prince Rupert had landed his passengers just before dawn, and that the entire party had gone into town in a rented car.

The air was bitter cold, though the sun shone bright and clear in the blue heavens. The smell of the fresh tingling air, the sight of firs and pines, the

waste hump-land spreading out around the town—
all this was a welcome sight for Thorne. Kincaid and
Simmons felt miserable because of the cold, but said
nothing in spite of their shivering.

At the hotel in Fort Norman the clerk reported
that the party of three with their dog had checked in,
changed into winter clothes, ate breakfast and left.
Thorne knew that a constable would have the men
under surveillance from the moment they arrived.
During breakfast in the hotel, he formulated a plan
with Kincaid. As neither Simmons nor Jack Kincaid
had ever been on snowshoes, Thorne put in a call
for a weasel from the Air Base for them. The sergeant
explained that it was important to get over to his
shack and make contact with his own Headquarters.
About eleven-thirty in the morning a weasel came
chugging up the street. Kincaid was fascinated with
the caterpillar-tracked machine and insisted on examining it from back to front.

An hour later the weasel pushed through the pine
forests into the outskirts of the town. When they
reached the shack, Silver Chief barked and cavorted
around as his master pushed open the door. The fact
that the door was unlocked was not lost on Jack and
Simmons. Everything, even the tea billy still sitting
on the potbellied stove, was as Thorne had left it
that fateful morning of the previous week. The two
Americans and the driver of the weasel followed
Thorne and Chief into the room, stamping the wet
snow from their feet.

Thorne immediately switched on the radio sending and receiving set, then set about building a fire
in the stove, using kindling from the woodbox on

the floor and larger pieces of wood from a box in the rear of the cabin.

As the fire caught on and started to blaze away cheerfully, Thorne put tea water on to boil. The radio had now warmed up by this time, and began cracking and spitting with static caused by the aurora borealis. Thorne sat down at the rough pine table and called Headquarters. At last he was answered.

"Come in, Thorne. Welcome back. We have a few reports for you. Inspector Corliss has called three times this morning, asking about you."

"Thanks. You all know who is up here with me. There is no point in going into names. Ask somebody to bring some bread and staples out to my shack. We're on our way as soon as you tell us what we're up here for."

Sergeant Thorne was purposely vague, realizing how clever and well organized the enemy was. He did not wish to divulge any more information than was absolutely necessary.

"You have a man on this case, don't you?" he continued.

"Is that supposed to be sarcastic, Sergeant? Of course we have."

"What's the latest report? We are trying to keep out of sight so they will lead us to what we are looking for . . ."

"I understand you perfectly. . . . The last report we had was that the three men and the dog were heading northwestward in the general direction of Great Bear Lake. We do not know what you are planning, but the pilot was sure that Jenkins signaled from about a quarter-mile behind them. We guess

Jenks didn't want to expose himself too much in case they had field glasses. The pilot said the trail looked fairly clear. A light snow has just started, with more on the way. The pilot got back into Fort Norman so that he could give us a good map fix. Have you the Army weasel?"

"Yes. The driver is right here with us. We are anxious to get started. I agree with you that if they are traveling out in the open and heading into the wilderness, they must have a fixed objective. We'd better get 'em quick. My feeling is that they are getting desperate and are ready for some final move."

Thorne could see Kincaid out of the corner of his eye as he spoke into the microphone. Jack was nodding in agreement.

"O.K., Thorne," crackled the voice from Headquarters. "You'd better all stick together. We have a weather forecast of a heavy front coming down from the Arctic. It doesn't look good. Be sure the weasel's radio is working before you leave. We don't want any wireless blackouts, because the weather forecast indicates all planes will soon be grounded and we won't be able to send you help. Keep in hourly contact.

"Here's a short cut to where you should cross their trail. Take the weasel straight cross-country. The hump-land between lakes isn't too rough, and besides, all the lakes are frozen in thick enough to support the weasel easily. On your map of the area these are the grid co-ordinates. K-17 from the left and D-03 from the bottom up. See what it is? A long ravine opens up there. We figure the men will head down through the ravine, not only for shelter but for protection. You will be able to pick up their trail around in there. Got the spot?"

Thorne checked quickly with his dividers on his topographical survey map and arrived at the spot that had been described. He glanced at the map and saw that the fugitives were headed along the northern fringe of Great Bear Lake, to the left of Great Bear River, a country so wild and deserted that even wild animals were seldom seen in the wilderness of frozen lakes and barren land.

Thorne answered: "Got it, Tom. We'll be off in twenty minutes. I'll let you know what happens when we get there. Can't figure what they are up to in that country, but the best way to find out is to get up there and see. I estimate we'll be there in about an hour and a quarter."

Thorne clicked the radio off. He brought cups for everyone and poured his guests his own special concoction of strong-brewed Irish tea.

Jack took one sip from his mug and let out a howl of anguish.

"Pete! That stuff's hot and strong enough for the Devil himself to chase a mouse across."

Thorne smiled and went about getting them ready for their trip. "You all heard the report from Headquarters," he said. "So there is no need for me to repeat it. I don't have boots enough to go around, so please stay in the weasel. I have plenty of mitts, and here is a coat for each of you.

"If there is any fighting or action of any sort, please let me handle it. The driver has a Thompson submachine gun and knows how to use it. I don't have any bread for sandwiches so let's each take a couple of tins of bully beef and some biscuits. It will hold us off for a while. If we have to, I can probably find some foot leaves out in the open and boil them into tea."

The weasel driver, who up to that moment had been silent, made a comment.

"We carry a survival kit, you know, Sergeant, also emergency rations. There are two bedrolls, and parkas if you need them. However, the cabin of the weasel is heated."

Sergeant Thorne thanked the driver.

There was a great scurry and bustle getting into coats, adjusting scarves, gulping tea, and all the other last-minute details before a man hunt.

Sergeant Thorne, now back in his own element, proceeded with calm assurance. He tucked his map in a case. Next he strapped his own antimagnetic compass on his wrist. Checked his rifle with its telescopic sights. Then he belted on his own service revolver, with its familiar, well-worn stock. It felt friendly and reassuring after the cold, impersonal plastic-handled ones like the American .45 he had been carrying.

Kincaid and Simmons quietly took their positions inside the weasel. Thorne helped Silver Chief up on the cumbersome land vessel.

With a roar and a clank of treads, the weasel chugged off into the silent woods. Thorne indicated the general direction they were to take. Silver Chief sat up on the bow savoring the wind, where the fine powdered snow coated and sheathed him in a white mantle. Even though the temperature was 15 degrees below zero, Silver Chief was warm and snug in his beautiful thick white coat and was enjoying every minute of the trip.

The passengers in the weasel rode in silence. Thorne, however, frequently glanced out at the sky. He noted that the snow was beginning to thicken as they rode through an occasional open space in the woods.

For an hour they bumped and clanked along, over hill, down dale, across frozen ponds, small lakes, up drifted snowbanks, over rotted timber with bone-jarring but relentless progress.

After an hour had passed, the countryside began to change. The woods thinned out, broad plateaus and deep ravines made their appearance. Because of the nature of the terrain, Thorne could see that they were approaching the western tip of Great Bear Lake, one of the largest fresh-water bodies of water in the world. He asked the driver to slow down as he put on snow goggles and kept a close watch on his side of the weasel. The others scanned for tracks on their side as they crept along, and Simmons called for a sudden halt near a clump of frozen bracken. When the weasel ground to a stop a few feet from the bushes, Silver Chief jumped off into the snow. Thorne followed into the open, where wind-driven pellets of cold struck his face. He walked toward the bushes, with Simmons directing to the lee side, to a place where signs showed clearly that a party had recently stopped for shelter. The ground, even though the snow had almost filled in the footprints, was disturbed and beaten down.

As the sergeant was examining the prints, Kincaid checked the scene through his piece of glass.

"We've hit it, Peter. Right on the nose!" Jack cried. "The whole area is covered with telltale green. I can even follow a small amount on the trail they left. Come on, let's get going!"

Thorne, who was now staring through his own eyepiece, nodded in agreement. He walked back to hoist himself up onto the weasel, but he first turned to call Silver Chief. Noting his dog's attitude, Thorne paused before letting out a cry, for Silver Chief stood tense and still as marble in the snow, every hair along his spine and neck bristling. The sergeant called to him, but unlike his usually obedient self, Chief completely ignored the summons. Instead of returning to his master, he started circling the bracken, each time making a wider arc. Now Thorne kept absolutely still, watching his dog go through the timeless method of finding a lost or elusive scent.

Kincaid leaned out of the weasel and spoke with some impatience.

"Come on, Peter. Get your dog aboard and let's get cracking!"

Brushing aside this request, Thorne continued to watch Silver Chief, who had by this time extended his radius beyond the weasel and its occupants. When he was at right angles to the snowmobile, he stopped and stiffened again, his nose searching the wind, every sense awake and concentrated. The dog suddenly broke and ran a hundred feet downwind to a smaller clump of bracken, trotted around it once, gave a savage growl and glanced back at his master.

The sergeant called again, and when Chief made no move to return, Thorne suddenly made up his mind. He reached up on the deck of the weasel to pull loose a pair of snowshoes he had thrown there.

This action made Kincaid half rise from his seat.

"Peter, what are you doing? Have you gone crazy? Get that dog in here and let's go. What are you trying to prove? There's the trail directly ahead."

Thorne did not answer.

"Driver, hand me down that rifle," he demanded. The Canadian handed down the rifle without question. Then and only then did Thorne reply.

"I realize, Jack, that time is of the essence. I also agree that there is a trail directly ahead. Scientifically, you are right in wanting to pursue it. However, Silver Chief has discovered that the trail branches . . ."

"So what?" Jack interrupted. "You're wasting time."

"Not at all," Sergeant Thorne replied calmly and mildly. "I will stake my life on the fact that Silver Chief is right. He has never failed me yet."

"So it boils down to whether we trust every scientific means of completing this case by following the trail ahead or of chasing after your dog on a probable wild-goose chase."

"Exactly!" Thorne snapped his jaws shut as he saw the muscles tighten on Kincaid's face. The two men stared steadily, each gauging the other's strength. For a few moments neither gaze fell but remained locked in a struggle of wills.

Kincaid seemed to have a logical advantage on his side—the machine gun, the driver, and Simmons, young, strong and intelligent—yet this was one time when the Royal Canadian Mounted Police would not be swayed. With cool assurance the sergeant continued to stare at his friend, until Kincaid decided to compromise and end the dramatic struggle of wills.

"I can't argue with you, Pete. This is your ball park. When you came down and played in our league you kept your mouth shut and listened and learned. O.K., Sergeant. I won't get in your way. You've got the greatest dog I've ever laid eyes on. If you're willing to stake your life, your job, your Government, and possibly the fate of the free world on something Silver Chief can see that we can't, then I say go to it.

"I'm from Texas myself, Sergeant, and I'm going to stick it out with what I can see and follow."

Abruptly Jack Kincaid leaned out and over the weasel and pulled off his mitten to shake hands. Sergeant Thorne returned the handclasp briskly, without thinking. Kincaid let out a yelp of pain and dropped back in his seat. The twenty seconds' exposure to the cold, bitter air had left his hand half frozen.

After the weasel had pulled off, clanking away into the northeast, Thorne bent down and strapped on his snowshoes. By the time he had straightened up, slung his rifle across his back and settled everything tight and at the "ready," he could barely see his former partner looking through his tinted glass at the distant trail ahead.

"All right now, Chief. Here we go. I agree with you. Where that Russian dog goes, there we will find our large cross-eyed bully. You know best, my trusted friend. Now is the time to prove it." He patted Chief lovingly on the head.

"If you fail, I fail. If I fail, I have a feeling we all fail. Something tells me the other trail is a decoy. Too plain and obvious. Eh, Chief? These chaps have shown us that they know what they are doing and have a reason for everything. Why is the trail so obvious even now with the snow falling? Lead on, Chief. Get 'em, boy. Go get 'em."

With a bound, Silver Chief was off through the snow, head high, then low, coursing right, coursing left, but always forging ahead. Frequently the sergeant forced Silver Chief to stop so that he could take a map and compass reading. With infinite care and patience he took out his map and drew a line; since he recognized some salient feature of the adjacent terrain, Thorne could pin-point it on the map.

After the third map check the sergeant could see that they were skirting the south shore of the vast frozen area of Great Bear Lake. The sun was very low in the west, even though it was only one-thirty in the afternoon. Thorne was also aware that darkness set in very quickly in the frozen tundra of the Northland. He also realized there was little daylight left.

So he decided on a bold course. A glance at the map showed that the mouth of the fast-flowing Great Bear River lay almost directly ahead. He was aware that the fugitives could never cross the torrent of the Great Bear River, where the lake emptied into it. He also knew that if his deductions were correct, his long-sought-for enemy was trapped somewhere ahead and not too far away.

Thirty minutes later he could see the vast frozen

expanse of Great Bear Lake almost in front of him. The bare, drab tundra gave way to a fringe of trees along the lake shore—dwarf pines, twisted spruce, knotted firs. Three times Thorne saw signs of life, only to find that a lonely caribou, cut off from the herd, had wandered along the shore line seeking food in this meager land.

As Thorne and Silver Chief came abreast of the lake and skirted the lonely shore, the sergeant became troubled by some subconscious thought. A sixth sense warned him to slow down and walk slowly and carefully. Suddenly he froze in his steps and ducked behind a grotesque dwarf pine. The reason came to him with the force of a blow what had been plaguing him for at least five minutes. Smoke! Where there is smoke there is fire! A truer saying was never uttered. And where there is fire, there is man, for no natural cause could make a fire burn in that desolate waste country.

Thorne glanced at Silver Chief and saw that he too was set into immobility, testing and sampling the wind, which came to them downwind off the gleaming whiteness of the frozen lake. Using every bit of wood lore he possessed, Peter Thorne started up the snow-drifted incline ahead, confident that on the other side of the hill he would find his quarry. He dare not even make the motions necessary to unsling his rifle, since he still could be seen. Rather he thought it better to assume a position where he could do the observing instead of being observed.

Slowly dog and man worked their way up the slope. Thorne knew that at the top there lay a narrow ex-

panse of crest with thirty or forty feet of hard bare
earth, and that there was a downward slope on the
other side, which he guessed would be the shore line
of the lake.

He examined the ground as carefully as the falling
snow would permit, and decided it would be safer
to skirt around the crest and plan to come halfway
down the slope on the other side. From there he
would also be downwind and could make any moves
necessary without exposing himself. As he glanced
up to indicate change of direction to Chief, Thorne
caught sight of a vague silhouette—a sight that almost made his heart stop beating!

Standing against the farthermost tree before the
clearing was Chelkar! Mushroom-brown in color, he
stood almost perfectly camouflaged against the trunk.
Immovable, yet thoroughly alert, Chelkar was the
classic picture of a ruthless, working watchdog. Were
it not for the fact that he was upwind from Thorne
and Silver Chief, he would now be tearing toward
them in attack.

Silver Chief sank into the snow as silently as the
falling flakes, and began to creep forward.

Peter Thorne knew that nothing could now per-
suade his dog from stalking the enemy. And indeed
it might be to his own advantage that the battle
should be joined. Yet as he gazed at the brute in front
of them, the sergeant realized that Chief's opponent
was a terrible and dangerous foe, one who might
indeed be victor in the fight. Neither he nor Silver
Chief would return alive unless their present plan
of action resulted in complete victory!

Whispering a silent, heartfelt "good luck" to his companion, Thorne quietly slid around the curve of the hill.

This was the hour of decision! There could be no turning back, no mistakes.

Chapter 17

REVENGE AT LAST

FROM the moment Silver Chief had caught the scent of Chelkar on the unconscious body of his master, hate for that ruthless guardian had lain deep in Chief's consciousness.

All dogs have instinctive reactions; they possess a sense which tells them if they are in the presence of a friend or enemy. Ordinarily, because of his superior intelligence and training, Chief got along well with strange dogs unless he was attacked. It was different with Chelkar. This hated intruder had committed an act that could never be forgiven or forgotten by brutally assaulting his master. And each time he crossed the path of his foe, Chief was filled with one desire alone. Revenge!

Once kindled, this spirit of revenge was given impetus by promptings of his wolf ancestry. Once again he seemed to be part of a yowling pack stalking his prey, without the restraint of training and discipline. Unlike Chelkar, whose training had been to track and kill only, Silver Chief's rancor was born of love and devotion.

As he inched forward on his haunches, he sized up

194

his enemy. The fates seemed to be favoring Chief's position, for the pale sun shone in Chelkar's eyes, and icy gales blowing downwind also aided the stealthy approach.

At one time Silver Chief had tangled with a vicious Doberman pinscher; Chelkar was similar in conformation, but larger and heavier.

Slower and closer Chief crept up the slope, time and again bellying in the snow, ears back and body blending perfectly with his natural habitat. . . . This was a game of life and death!

Like all well-trained watchdogs, Chelkar had a sixth sense of danger. He kept gazing about continuously, moving as if seeking shelter from the cold but actually keeping on the alert for unwelcome intruders.

Aware that within seconds he might be discovered, Chief's body tensed. The cunning of his wolf ancestors now prompted him. Suddenly he stopped dead in his tracks; this was the moment to attack! With a low involuntary growl he sprang forward, lunging to take Chelkar on the flank not only with his full weight but with the added value of his opponent's unpreparedness.

Silver Chief's self-confidence almost lost the battle before it was fairly started. Not only was Chelkar fast enough to see what was coming, but he immediately took the offensive. Though thrown a trifle off balance by the speed of the attack, he recovered quickly, throwing his front paws and fending Chief off, in the manner of a boxer. Chief swept past the larger dog and, in doing so, was dealt a stunning blow on the side of the head by Chelkar's huge paw that sent him rolling in the snow. Chief was instantly on his feet again, using the momentum to set him straight.

Chelkar was on him with the speed of lightning, slashing, biting, crowding. The two ferocious animals fought toe-to-toe for several minutes, neither giving or gaining an inch. As they feinted, ripped and sparred, each trying to get some sort of hold on the other, Silver Chief sensed that he must quickly change his tactics. If he didn't do this, he knew that the more powerful dog, wise in the tricks of infighting and using his brute strength to advantage, would surely wear him out. If he were fatigued, it would be easy to make a slip. Only one was needed!

Much to Chelkar's surprise, Silver Chief deliberately broke off the slugging match and backed away. The other dog stood for a second, a cruel, triumphant gleam in his eyes. Then he charged. No mincing and guarding now—he charged direct, intent on one thing only—Silver Chief's jugular vein, to rip the lifeblood from this deadly enemy.

Silver Chief met the blunt, head-on charge halfway, and gave ground slightly to the left, testing to see if his opponent had a weak or blind side. Chelkar grabbed at his neck and caught a mouthful of fur. Still yanking at Silver Chief's throat, he tried to throw him, but he lost his grip when Chief's neck fur came loose. Chief counterattacked instantly. He felt flesh tear and give; he had almost severed an ear from Chelkar's head.

Silver Chief could feel the fury in his enemy as he pressed home his attack. Blood was now pouring down Chelkar's head, but that fact did not seem to hamper the huge dog's fighting ability. He met the onslaught with his boxer's defense, something that Silver Chief had never encountered in any other dog fight. Once again the larger dog cuffed Chief on the head and knocked him off balance, and this time Chelkar was ready.

Chelkar did not pause to follow up his advantage but sprang like a great cloud of doom, ripping and tearing at Chief's body wherever he could attack. Silver Chief could feel a knifelike pain across his backbone, then one on his side as his larger and more powerful enemy kept pressing his advantage.

Twisting and turning in every way possible did not help. Finally a log tripped Chief as he turned back to fight off Chelkar, and he was down in the snow, with Chelkar closing in for the kill.

The snow swirled and sprayed about in a cloud at the base of the log. Silver Chief could feel the hot, fetid breath of Chelkar as his enemy pressed down on him. He could see the sharp, stained fangs coming nearer and nearer, as they tangled and fought their death struggle in the lonely wilderness.

An excruciating pain tore through Silver Chief's left front paw. Chelkar had at last come to grips. Frantically Silver Chief struggled and kicked out with every ounce of strength he possessed to free himself. His hind feet found Chelkar's belly. He raked the dog's underbelly unmercifully as he kicked and struggled under Chelkar's weight. Then he could feel his claws ripping deep into Chelkar's flesh.

With an agonized howl of pain, Chelkar was forced to drop Chief's paw from his jaws. In a flash Silver Chief bounded to his feet. Instead of closing in again

to the attack, he raced away out into the open clearing where he could have more room to maneuver. He knew that if he were downed again it would be the end of him.

Chelkar advanced slowly, not flinching or wearying of the attack, but more wary this time. He noticed the limp that Silver Chief tried to conceal, so from then on all the fighting and attacking would be directed at Silver Chief's left side to exploit the weakness.

Again and again Chelkar closed in, reared up,

snapped and backed away, always directing his attack
at Silver Chief's bleeding paw. He was trying to tire
Silver Chief out to make him expend his precious
energy by beating off the constant cunning attacks.

Each time Silver Chief strove to turn the tide of
the battle and take the offense himself, Chelkar
would step back or give ground, never allowing his
opponent to close. Chelkar was playing a cat-and-
mouse game and thoroughly enjoying himself.

At this point Silver Chief became a completely
savage creature. His wily timber wolf ancestry took

over, warning that to succeed and stay alive, he would have to trick his awesome opponent.

Now his tactics changed again and he charged Chelkar more carelessly, using a more open attack.

With each attack Chelkar gave way in the hope of tiring his opponent, but he did not press the fight. This was precisely in line with Silver Chief's stratagem. It was his plan to make each attack seem that he was more feeble, each recovery slower and more dispirited.

On about the fourth advance he whirled past Chelkar and recovered with deliberately slow ineptitude. Chelkar leaped in, snarling with triumph and hate. Chief maneuvered his head so that his opponent would aim for the heavy fur coat at his neck and consequently would be unlikely to grasp more than a slight amount of flesh. When Chief was certain that the crazed dog had as good a grip as possible, he suddenly went limp, turning himself into what seemed to be a broken, defeated mass.

Chelkar fell for the ruse. He shook and tore with the frenzy of a killer. At last, feeling no response to his vicious motions, he dropped Chief's body in the snow.

Silver Chief instantly sprang up at his enemy, who was so taken by surprise that he made no attempt to defend himself. Before he could even brace himself to slash back, Silver Chief was up and under him.

With a crunching snap of his jaw, Silver Chief felt Chelkar's neck muscles give way on the soft underside, but he continued to tear through flesh and bones as he shook the life out of the wildly thrashing, fear-crazed dog in his grip. Thrashing, kicking, yanking,

Chelkar tried every other trick that he knew, but to no avail. Grimly Silver Chief held on to his enemy.

Soon the thrashing about became feeble and then nonexistent. Chelkar sank to his knees, to his side, and breathing ceased. The fight was over.

Silver Chief too lay for a few minutes in the snow, trembling from excitement and the letdown after battle.

At last he got up and completely circled his fallen foe, sniffing at the mangled body, to be sure he had completely finished the job. Slowly, then, without a backward look, he limped off down the slope of the hill, to pick up his master's trail.

Silver Chief had taken his revenge!

Chapter 18

BROUGHT TO BAY

STEALTHILY Sergeant Thorne crept through the snow, taking cover at every opportunity as he circled round the hill to the lake shore. Eventually he came out on the bank overlooking the frozen expanse of Great Bear Lake. The lightly falling snow, however, obscured the far-distant opposite shore.

Not daring to expose himself, Thorne made no attempt to scan beyond the embankment, in an effort to locate the source of the smoke. Instead, he crept toward the faint markings of a path, which by its direction should lead down to the shore line itself.

In front of him stood a cluster of weather-beaten pines, their stunted formation seeming as one with the group of grubby bushes growing in their center. If he used their protection as a vantage point, he would have a better over-all view of the terrain.

Once inside the shelter of the bushes, the sergeant unslung his rifle and sighted the telescopic lenses along the trail leading to the lake. As he crouched there, he had a wide vista of frozen countryside. So intent was Thorne on observing the frozen landscape that he started when a voice from behind spoke in cold, menacing tones.

"Do not make a move. Clasp your hands behind your neck and keep them there."

The sergeant dropped his gun and turned slowly. The man approaching held a revolver steadily in his hand. His attitude was one of complete self-assurance.

"What are you doing on other people's property?" the stranger demanded in clipped and precise English.

Thorne could not be certain if this was one of the enemy, but his thoughts raced ahead to include such a possibility. Perhaps this arrogant fellow had been set on the slope as guard; if so, his Comrades would not be far off. To deny the reality of his suspicions, Thorne kept his tones reasonable when he said, "I don't know who you are. I am a Royal Canadian Mounted Police Sergeant. If I am actually trespassing, I can only apologize and leave." With this explanation the sergeant started to lower his hands and raise himself up from the crouching position.

The man with the gun ordered sharply, "Just keep your hands up and come with me!"

As he waved to indicate that Thorne should move out from the copse, the sergeant acted on impulse, and twisted as if he meant to rise. Instead, he let himself down and, sliding a few feet, kicked his leg out and tripped the man. As the stranger toppled over into the snow, Thorne retrieved his gun and struck the man on the head with such a force that he never knew what hit him. Then he stooped over and took the unconscious man's revolver and slipped it into his pocket.

Hurriedly the sergeant glanced about; evidently no one had observed the scuffle. Yet it was too late to retrace his steps, for he heard someone laboring up the path calling to Chelkar.

Thorne crouched down in the snow, every sense alert. Moments later he spied a familiar blue woolen cap, the face—with its crossed eye and gaping mouth —for which he had diligently searched across the North American Continent.

This time the element of surprise was reversed and Thorne did the attacking. Illych let out one grunt of enraged surprise before Thorne was upon him like some avenging fury. Straight into the heavy, puffed face he drove his hammerlike fist. The blow caught Illych on the jaw, stunning him and forcing him back a step down the trail.

Reeling from the blow, the Russian groped blindly for his hated enemy, hoping to be able to overcome him by brute strength. Wisely Peter Thorne avoided the bearlike arms, side-stepping to shoot a left hook into Illych's face just below the eye. Thorne had the satisfaction of feeling flesh and bone give way under this crunching blow.

Again Illych was forced to give back as blood spurted from his cheek, and he bellowed with rage and surprise, "Chelkar! Lackvief!"

Thorne smiled. Illych could cry out in vain for his lackey guard now lying unconscious in the snow near the bushes.

Illych made a desperate try to regain the offensive; this was his undoing. As the huge man lunged forward, he slipped, and shifted his gaze for an instant. This moment was all that the sergeant needed. He threw his right squarely into Illych's blood-sodden face, putting every bit of the fighting power of his back and legs into the blow. With a look of dazed surprise Illych toppled over backward to roll down the remaining fifteen feet of embankment. He lay still.

Thorne raced down the trail to the side of his enemy. He leaned over, unhooked Illych's belt, using it to bind the arms of his now thoroughly beaten enemy. Convinced that this would hold him for a while, Thorne traced the source of the smoke, which came from a cave running into the bank. The entrance to this hide-out in the rocks was camouflaged with a wooden door painted to blend in with the embankment.

Drawing his revolver, the sergeant kicked open the door, which instantly gave way. A quick look around the cozy, scooped-out meeting place convinced him that no one else was there. After rummaging through piles of clothing, Thorne discovered belts and a leather strap which had been part of a camera case; these would do well to make his prisoners more secure.

First he returned to Illych, who had not moved from his crumpled position in the snow. Deftly Thorne bound his captive's legs as he said, "Just lie there and don't try any funny business. I'm going up to get your Comrade Lackvief before he freezes."

Thorne scrambled up the trail to where the unconscious man still sprawled close to the clump of bushes. After binding him securely, Thorne lifted the awkward burden to his back. Just as he started down the frozen bank, Silver Chief plodded slowly out of the woods, limping from his wound, but overjoyed to see his master.

After dumping the trussed-up load on a bunk inside the cave, Thorne returned for Illych. When he
carried him in and placed him alongside his comrade,
the sergeant ordered Silver Chief to watch the prisoners while he investigated further.

Thorne discovered that this hide-out was a series
of adjoining caves, the one next to the bunk room
used for stores, with shelves stocked from the floor to
the rounded roof with enough canned goods to last
throughout the winter.

Another door leading into the small adjacent cave
was securely boarded to keep out the bitter cold.
This was the nerve center of the place, with radio
equipment covering one wall. Two pilot lights flickered, showing that recent messages had been received.
On the other side of the cave was a sending-receiving
set of a kind Sergeant Thorne had never seen. From
a deep powerful hum, he knew that this huge communication outfit was now turned on. As he watched
it, Thorne observed that at periods of five seconds a
needle on the panel jumped to life, sounding a shrill
"beep." Since he was not familiar with the way the
set was operated, he did not attempt to touch the
knobs. Instead, he turned his attention to the short-
wave set, one of a more familiar make. He tuned into
one frequency and quickly raised Headquarters,
which came through remarkably clear. On the second
try the clarity of sound was astonishing. It was as if
the men at Headquarters were standing in the cave
and articulating with special emphasis.

"Thorne . . . come in. Thorne . . . come in. We
read you loud and clear. Where are you? . . . Give
us a position. . . . We've made contact with the

weasel. They have captured a Russian agent and are waiting for you at the position where you and your dog left the trail. They want to contact you at once. How are you calling us?"

Sergeant Thorne smiled at the enthusiasm of his unseen friend.

"Not too many questions, Red. I don't know my precise location, and never mind how I'm broadcasting. I have this whole gang wrapped up. Have Headquarters contact Inspector Corliss to stand by for a further report from me."

Thorne continued. "Tell the weasel I am roughly a mile and a half from them. Tell them to skirt Great Bear Lake in a southeasterly direction. I'm almost at the junction of the lake and Great Bear River. I'll be watching for them. It's going to be dark in less than an hour, so tell 'em to snap it up. Will report later. Over and out."

"Right, Sergeant. Will contact them now. Just follow around the lake shore. Is that it?"

"Roger."

After this talk Thorne resumed his investigation. He was astonished to see how well the network of caves had suited the varied purposes of the enemy. He discovered another door, but a stout lock prevented his opening it. Perhaps Illych had the keys. Returning to the bunk room he went through the Russian's pockets and found a case containing four keys. One of them fitted the door he wished to enter, and Thorne quickly opened it. He stuck his head into a dark, cold cavern, and groping, his hand came upon a switch. Thorne pressed it, and in the sudden light that flooded the place, he realized why the mys-

tery of this cavern had been preserved. There, prim
on its twin skis, the green-and-white bush plane
rested on the surface of the frozen lake. Not wanting
to take any chances, Thorne took his revolver as he
stepped down on the ice. He looked around atten-
tively; on a shelf built flush with the cavern wall was
a crate, roughly the size of the one that had been
taken from the lightning-blasted tree. He could see
at a glance that the box had been opened and then
renailed. Thorne took out his eyepiece and peered
at the innocent-looking object. Through the glass it
radiated tones of brilliant green!

As he stood there gazing in fascinated awe, the
sergeant heard a strange whining buzz that rose in
crescendo like some huge, unearthly mosquito. He
rushed to the radio room. The large, more powerful
set was emitting a hum that almost burst his ear-
drums.

Feeling a need to relax a moment after the feverish
activity, Thorne grabbed his rifle and stepped outside the cave. There, in the freezing dusk of early
afternoon, he scanned the skies, the land about, and
the far-off stretches of the silent lake. There was
nothing in the scene to indicate any intrusion upon
the peacefulness except the dim clank-clank of the
weasel, threading its way across the mountain.

Thorne realized he could not linger there. Caution
tugged him back indoors to recheck the bindings of
his prisoners. As he entered the cave, the sergeant
could feel a tension mounting, subtle and unexplained. It was as if the throbbing radio had communicated some climax to the Russian agents. Illych's
anger and frustration at being captured had given

way to furious hatred. Lackvief, who had returned
to consciousness, lay like one drugged and listening
to the voice of fantasy. Against this taut awareness,
the large radio now reached the pitch of some shrieking monster.

Thorne ordered Silver Chief to double his vigilance. He himself returned outdoors to try to intercept the weasel, which now could be heard quite
clearly. Halfway up the trail, he paused to look back.
He squinted and shaded his eyes. What seemed to
be a dot ten feet off the lake level approached with
incredible speed, its gnat-size enlarging into a sleek
plane that was bearing down almost faster than the
eye could follow.

Thorne stooped down on the trail and drew his
revolver. The oncoming plane did not bother to
circle or make a landing approach. Two wheels came
into view, and then a third as the landing gear was
lowered. Because of the complete absence of noise
he might have overlooked it entirely. When the plane
glided down onto the ice for its final approach, the
sergeant could see that it was completely black and
had no markings of any sort on the fuselage. As it
taxied toward the camouflaged cave entrance he realized that it was jet-propelled. Though trained in
aircraft identification, this one was completely unfamiliar to the sergeant. The whine of the twin jets
was distinct as the ship spun around toward the cave
entrance.

From the cockpit a blinker light flashed twice and
Thorne knew that the ship was asking for a recognition signal. When none came, the plexiglass canopy
suddenly slid back, revealing two heads. But before

the sergeant could raise his revolver, he heard the angry chatter of a Thompson submachine gun coming from above. He could see the red tracer bullets plunking into the plane and could hear Jack Kincaid's excited voice. At the first sound of the bullets the canopy snapped shut, and the plane spun grimly on its axis, creating an explosive whirl of loose snow. With a blast of power such as Thorne had never imagined, the plane gathered speed along the ice, its twin jets at full throttle. It was airborne within five hundred yards. Instead of seeking altitude, the plane banked superbly at fifty or sixty feet and headed due west, streaking into the gathering dusk with incredible speed. In twenty seconds it was gone.

From above on the tip of the bank, Kincaid stood shouting at the top of his lungs.

"Pete . . . Pete . . . Where are you?"

The words were followed by Kincaid himself, accompanied by the cocky weasel driver, who toted his wicked Tommy gun. The three men stood at the foot of the trail on the shore of the lake.

"You know what that plane was, Pete, or where it came from?"

Thorne looked his friend gravely in the eye.

"I'm not sure, Jack, but I have a pretty good idea," he answered. "That was Russia's newest, long-range, jet fighter bomber. They must have flown all the way from Siberia or Russia at less than fifty feet altitude, to sneak under our Inter-Continental Radar Net. Whew! Think of the navigation of flying that ship!"

The sergeant led Jack and the driver to the door of the cave.

"This was the last desperate act of this gang, and

explained their reason for returning here to Fort
Norman. When I take you through this door, you
will see something that will make your eyes pop. I
am almost glad that plane got away."

Jack Kincaid looked keenly at his partner. "Why,
Pete?"

Thorne rested his hand on the door. "Because,
Jack, anything else might have meant war."

"That's possible," Kincaid admitted, "but I know
our Air Force would give a lot to grab that Tupelov
4-Twelve."

"True," Thorne said, "but we have the dikortrium
and they don't. The leader of the gang is now my
prisoner—the same man who helped plan the murder of Pilot Landry. Those were the jobs I was
assigned to, and with the help of you and Silver
Chief, they've been accomplished. Now you and
Simmons come inside and see what you will see!"

Thorne held the door open and followed Kincaid
and the driver into the cave. After giving a brief satisfied look at the surly prisoners, Jack headed toward
the humming sound in the cave beyond. Seeing the
complex maze of communication systems in such a
small area made him whistle in disbelief.

"This is the most fantastic setup I've ever seen,"
he said. "It must have taken them years to assemble
all this stuff and get it rigged up. The work involved
is almost unbelievable! This must be one of the
major subterranean Headquarters of the enemy."

"That's been my idea since I first came upon it,"
Thorne told him. "Maybe the notion of such a setup
was in the back of my mind all the while, urging me
to return to Canada."

"Something sure was in the back of your mind," Jack returned.

"This is how I figure it, Jack. Back in the days when Russia was going to all lengths to obtain the secret of the atomic bomb, Canada allowed the information to leak out that she had this large area of uranium deposits. I wouldn't be surprised if this base has been operating since then."

"It's more than possible," Jack agreed.

Thorne gave a sudden wide, infectious grin. "Well, they didn't get away with it," he said. "But look, Jack, you and Simmons help me lift this crate, won't you? Let's get it out of here and then the prisoners. I have to make a report before I can wrap up this case."

Later, when the crate, the Russians and as much equipment as possible had been loaded on the weasel, Kincaid came to the sergeant's side. Jack lit up a cigarette, and after inhaling deeply, he spoke in a low tone.

"Peter, I owe you an apology."

"How come?"

"Well, I was pretty cocky a little while ago. If you had followed my advice we would have been in bad shape now. That trail on the north side of the lake was a decoy. We picked up Jenkins, your constable, who had also fallen for the ruse. If you had played my way, the plane would now be headed for Siberia with the dikortrium aboard. The agents here wouldn't have cared what we did with them then. You called the tricks!"

"As a matter of fact," the sergeant said thoughtfully, "it was Silver Chief who showed me the way."

"Well, anyhow," Kincaid went on. "I learned a good lesson. It is that faith sometimes guides us more wisely than statistics and machines. It's a good lesson, Peter, and I want to thank you."

"Nonsense, Jack. It was co-operation that turned the tide. I wish all countries could learn the value of working together."

"So do I," Kincaid agreed heartily, as the two shook hands with a warm understanding clasp.